A BIOLOGY OF CRUSTACEA

ASPECTS OF ZOOLOGY
SERIES

A BIOLOGY OF CRUSTACEA
J. Green, B.Sc., Ph.D.

INSECT SOUNDS
P. T. Haskell, B.Sc., Ph.D.

SOIL ANIMALS
D. Keith McE. Kevan, B.Sc.,
Ph.D., A.I.C.T.A.,
F.R.S.Edin.

In preparation
A BIOLOGY OF DRAGONFLIES
P. S. Corbet, B.Sc., Ph.D.

A BIOLOGY OF CRUSTACEA

by

J. GREEN

B.Sc., Ph.D.

Zoology Dept., Bedford College, University of London

H. F. & G. WITHERBY LTD

First published in 1961 by
H. F. & G. WITHERBY LTD
5 Warwick Court, London, W.C.1

©

H. F. & G. WITHERBY LTD. 1961

PRINTED IN GREAT BRITAIN BY
NORTHUMBERLAND PRESS LIMITED
GATESHEAD ON TYNE

To
MARY,
RACHEL and HELEN

PREFACE

THIS book is but one of several biologies of Crustacea that might be written. The choice of material for inclusion has been a personal one, and has been biased by my own interests. It follows that no attempt has been made to be all embracing. There are, doubtless, many other topics which might justifiably have been included, but I make no apology for their absence; the space allowed is not unlimited, and the treatment of some topics is already over-condensed.

While I am not much troubled by what has been omitted, I am deeply conscious of the possibility of error in what has been included; if I have misinterpreted anyone's work I should be grateful for being corrected.

As a general rule the aim has been to deal with those aspects of biology which concern the whole intact animal. Occasional excursions are made to the interior of the animal, but only in order to explain what is happening to the whole animal. The chapter on blood and circulation is included because the hearts of many crustaceans are visible in the intact animal and can be seen functioning, likewise the striking changes in the haemoglobin content of *Daphnia* are easily observed. This chapter owes much to the sustained interest aroused when I was privileged to work for several years in the department of Prof. H. Munro Fox, F.R.S., who has also built up a small but well-selected collection of Crustacea, many of which have been used to prepare the illustrations for this book.

The selection of references for the literature lists at the end of each chapter has been difficult. In general those selected are fairly recent and in English, and usually easily obtainable, but a few references to the European literature have been included, either because they describe classical work, or else give information which is not yet available in English. Sometimes I have mentioned an author in the text without giving a reference at the end of the chapter; in this case the reference is given in one of the recent papers in the list, and it is usually fairly obvious which one should be consulted.

vii

Dr. B. M. Gilchrist has most kindly read the greater part of the manuscript and has given most helpful and constructive criticism. I am most grateful to her for helping to improve some of my more obscure paragraphs.

CONTENTS

LIST OF PLATES

ACKNOWLEDGMENTS

It has not been possible to prepare all the illustrations from specimens; a number have been copied from other sources, which I am pleased to acknowledge below.

The following authors have kindly given permission for me to copy their original illustrations: Dr. D. Atkins, Dr. H. Barnes, Professor H. G. Cannon, Professor R. Dennell, and Dr. H. Sanders.

My thanks are also due to the Royal Society of London for permission to reproduce figs. 1 and 19c (after D. J. Scourfield) and fig. 17 (after H. G. Cannon); to the Royal Society of Edinburgh for permission to reproduce figs. 20 and 22 from volume 55 of the *Transactions of the Royal Society of Edinburgh*, and fig. 21 from volume 59 of the same *Transactions*; to the Company of Biologists for permission to reproduce fig. 41 from the paper by W. Burke in the *Journal of Experimental Biology* (1954) volume 31; to the Zoological Society of London for permission to reproduce fig. 48 (after J. Green) and fig. 52 (after D. Atkins); to the University of Bergen for fig. 46 from G. O. Sars' *Crustacea of Norway*; to Messrs. A. & C. Black for permission to reproduce fig. 35 from Calman's section on Crustacea in Lankester's *Treatise of Zoology*; and to Messrs. Methuen & Co. for fig. 57 from Calman's *Life of Crustacea*.

INTRODUCTION

M o s t people have seen a crustacean at one time or another; crabs, lobsters, shrimps and woodlice are common enough, but there are also myriads of smaller less conspicuous Crustacea unknown to the layman. The aquarist probably knows *Daphnia* as 'the water flea' and does not consider it as a relative of the lobster.

Why are such different creatures included in the same group? One answer would be that they both have external skeletons and jointed limbs—features which they share with other arthropods such as insects, spiders and centipedes; they also have other similarities such as a pair of mandibles which act as jaws, and they have two pairs of appendages in front of the mouth—characters which distinguish them from other arthropods. But such an answer, although it is technically correct, is not very satisfying. In order really to understand why water fleas and lobsters belong to the same group it is necessary to know about other creatures belonging to the group and to know about their various ways of life.

In this book an attempt is made to treat the biology of Crustacea as a whole. The difficulties of this approach will become evident in the first chapter on origin and radiation; the origin may be obscure, but the results of their radiation abound throughout the world. No other class of animals exhibits such diversity of form. Nevertheless the essential unity of the Crustacea as a group becomes more apparent the more one learns of them.

CHAPTER I

ORIGIN AND RADIATION

I N the state of British Columbia there are certain rocks, the Burgess Shales, which were laid down over four hundred million years ago. These rocks are remarkable for the fossils which they contain. Some of these fossils look very similar to Crustacea which are alive to-day. The age of the Burgess Shales takes us back to within a comparatively few million years from the beginning of the detailed fossil record. This means that we cannot expect to get much information from fossils about the actual origin of the Crustacea, for the presence of these highly organised creatures so near to the beginning of the fossil record indicates that many features of the crustacean type of organisation were already in existence. But first we have the problem of whether these early fossils were, or were not Crustacea.

A satisfactory definition to include all Crustacea is extraordinarily hard to frame, because so many of them have become highly modified, particularly those which are parasitic. However, most Crustacea have, at least at some stage, two pairs of appendages in front of the mouth, which are called the antennules and the antennae. Generally too there are at least two or three pairs of appendages near to the mouth which have special functions in feeding. The first of these appendages are the mandibles, which function in the same manner as jaws with teeth, but working from side to side instead of up and down. Two pairs of maxillae lie behind the mandibles and are usually concerned in pushing food into the mouth. Now if we try to study these appendages in the early fossils we meet an insuperable obstacle. Although many of these fossils are beautifully preserved they do not provide us with the necessary details concerning the mouthparts—if indeed they ever had any mouthparts!

For this and other reasons many authorities prefer to include all the Burgess Shale fossils which look like Crustacea in a group called the Pseudocrustacea, and to ally this group with those remarkably abundant fossils the trilobites.

The trilobites were at one time thought to be Crustacea, but they are now regarded as being off the main line of crustacean descent. They have, for instance only a single pair of antennae in front of the mouth. The other head appendages do not differ very much from those on the rest of the body, so that they cannot be said to be separately modified for feeding, and there are no mandibles. We can thus exclude the trilobites from the Crustacea, and for the moment leave open the question as to whether they are anywhere near to the ancestral forms from which the Crustacea arose. Before we tackle this problem it will be as well to have a look at some of the early undoubted Crustacea.

The best description of an early fossil crustacean is undoubtedly Scourfield's description of *Lepidocaris rhyniensis*. This description was built up from an examination of thousands of fragments of Rhynie Chert. This is a rock which was produced about 300 million years ago in a region with springs containing water saturated with silica. Various animals and plants in this area have been incredibly well preserved as the water evaporated and the Chert was formed. The Chert is somewhat transparent, so that flakes can be examined under the microscope and fragments of *Lepidocaris* can be seen, often in fine detail, down to the hairs on certain bristles. *Lepidocaris* was a small crustacean, not quite reaching a length of three millimetres. The body was narrow and tapered and was divided into 19 segments. The head bore two pairs of appendages in front of the mouth; the antennules were small, but the antennae were large and branched, looking very like the antennae of modern water fleas (p. 5), so that they were probably used for swimming. The mouth-parts consisted of a pair of mandibles which had milled surfaces for breaking up food, and two pairs of maxillae, the second of which were very small. In the male the first maxillae formed claspers for gripping the female. Eleven pairs of legs lay behind

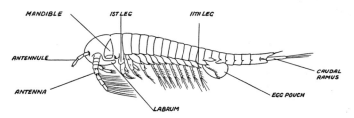

FIG. 1. *Lepidocaris rhyniensis*, lateral view of female. Actual length about three millimetres. (After Scourfield, 1926).

the maxillae; the first three pairs were broad with scraping spines at the tip, while the others each had two flaps and resembled the swimming legs of modern copepods (p. 7). The female carried an egg pouch on the underside of the body behind the legs. *Lepidocaris* is clearly a crustacean, and further, it can be classified as a member of the sub class Branchiopoda.

The Branchiopoda can be divided into various sub groups, and of these the Anostraca (fig. 2) show the greatest resemblance to *Lepidocaris*. They have narrow tapering bodies, with nineteen or more segments, and eleven, sometimes more pairs of legs. The maxillae are small, and the females carry their eggs in a pouch behind the legs. But there are also some differences. The Anostraca have stalked eyes, while no eyes were found in *Lepidocaris*. The

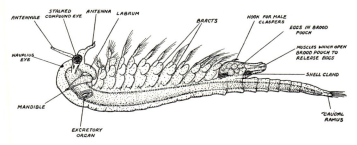

FIG. 2. *Artemia salina* (Anostraca), lateral view of female in the normal swimming position, with the back downwards. Actual length about 1 cm. Drawn from a specimen of the Californian stock reared in sea water.

male anostracan has the antennae, not the first maxillae, modified to form clasping organs, and the antennae of the female are not branched or used for swimming. In spite of such differences the similarities are great enough for *Lepidocaris* to be regarded as near to the stock from which the Anostraca arose. Unfortunately the Anostraca, although much larger than *Lepidocaris*, have very delicate skeletons and have not often been preserved as fossils. Such fossils as have been found do not help much with tracing the evolution of the group.

The other members of the Branchiopoda differ markedly from *Lepidocaris* and the Anostraca by having a carapace. This is a flap projecting from the back of the head and covering the body to a varying extent. In the Conchostraca the whole body and the limbs are enclosed within the carapace, which extends downwards

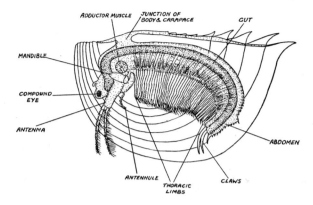

FIG. 3. *Limnadiopsis brichii* (Conchostraca), female with
the left valve of the carapace removed. Specimen from
Australia, actual length about 2 cm.

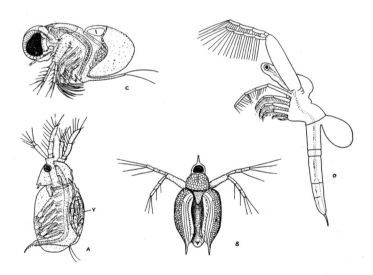

FIG. 4. Cladocera. A, *Sida crystallina*, female, lateral view; note
the young (Y) in the brood pouch. Actual length 3 mm. B,
Scapholeberis mucronata, female, ventral view. Actual length
1 mm. C, *Polyphemus pediculus*, lateral view of female with
empty brood pouch. Actual length 2 mm. D, *Leptodora kindti*,
female, lateral view. Actual length 9 mm.

on each side in the form of valves which can be drawn together by a muscle running across the body. Many fossils are known which look like Conchostraca and date from the Cambrian period (about 400 million years ago), but it is uncertain how many of these are true conchostracans because nothing is known about the limbs. However, it seems fairly certain that they were in existence at about the same time as *Lepidocaris*. The Cladocera (fig. 4) are smaller than the Conchostraca and have fewer limbs; the carapace is similar in form although it does not extend forwards to enclose

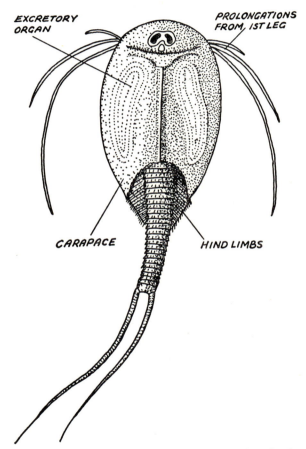

FIG. 5. *Triops granarius* (Notostraca) dorsal view. Specimen from South Africa, actual length 2.5 cm. excluding the caudal furca. The European species, *T. cancriformis*, has a relatively shorter body than this species.

the head. A few Cladocera have become predators with a reduced carapace enabling the legs to seize prey.

The Notostraca (fig. 5) have a different type of carapace which only covers the upper surface of the front of the body. They are odd in that the number of legs is not related to the number of segments; there may be 26-34 segments, but up to 71 pairs of legs. Although the general structure is so different from *Lepidocaris*, the legs bear a distinct resemblance to the first three pairs of this fossil (fig. 19, p. 27). The earliest definite fossil notostracans date from the Permian (about 200 million years ago). These are so similar to modern forms that they are placed in one of the two modern genera, and a slightly later fossil, from the Triassic (about 180 million years ago) is considered as actually belonging to the species *Triops cancriformis* which is widespread in Europe at present.

A recent discovery has been made in North America. *Hutchinsoniella macracantha* (fig. 8B) is a very peculiar little crustacean, living in soft mud in Long Island Sound; another species of its group has been found in San Francisco Bay. It is uncertain exactly where *Hutchinsoniella* fits in with the rest of the Crustacea, it has been assigned to a separate sub class, the Cephalocarida, but it undoubtedly has affinities with the Branchiopoda.

The ostracods (fig. 6) are the most abundant of the early fossil Crustacea, but most of them are not much help in tracing the origin and evolution of the group. Like the Conchostraca the ostracods have the body completely enclosed within a bivalved

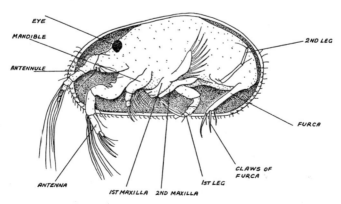

FIG. 6. *Heterocypris incongruens* (Ostracoda), female with the left valve of the carapace removed. Actual length 1.6 mm.

shell, and it is usually only the external form of the shell that is preserved. One notable exception is a series of 14 specimens described in 1876 by Brogniart. These were found in a silicified fruit from the Coal Measures of St. Etienne, and show a degree of preservation comparable with that of *Lepidocaris*. Ostracod shells have been described from the Upper Cambrian (about 400 million years ago), and over 3,000 species have been described from Palaeozoic rocks. They are also abundant to-day, both in fresh-water and the sea.

It is clear that we do not know enough about the early fossils to make a coherent story of the origin and primary radiation of

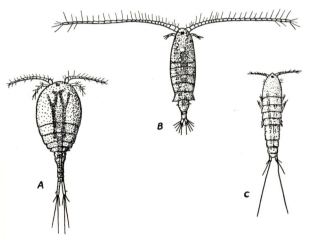

FIG. 7. Copepoda. A, a member of the Cyclopoida. B, a member of the Calanoida. C, a member of the Harpacticoida. A and B have an actual length of about 2.5 mm., while C is only 1 mm. long.

the Crustacea. We are confronted with the ostracods as abundant fossils early in the record, with *Lepidocaris* as a possible ancestral branchiopod, and with fossil Conchostraca occurring at about the same time. The situation is not helped when we look at other groups of Crustacea; the copepods (fig. 7) are practically unknown as fossils, and the cirripedes are so very distinct that relating them to any other group of Crustacea seems impossible. All that can be done is to study the radiation that has occurred within each of the groups.

There has been radiation of a spectacular nature within the

Copepoda. Some typical copepodan forms are illustrated in figs.
7A-C. The Cyclopoïda are almost monotonously alike, but it is
probably from this group that the majority of the parasitic forms
have evolved. The Calanoida are generally regarded as being
primitive; they have a heart, an organ not found in other copepods,
which are believed to have lost it during the course of their evolution. Of the non-parasitic groups, the Harpacticoidea show the
greatest range of form. Some are long and worm-shaped, others

TABLE I.

Geological Period	Time in millions of years	First positive records of Crustacea
	70	
Cretaceous		True Crabs (Brachyura)
	110	
Jurassic		Dromiid Crabs
		Pollicipes
	150	Many Decapoda Natantia (Cirripedia)
Triassic		Eryonidae *Triops cancriformis*
		Penaeid Prawns
Permian		Notostraca
	225	
Carboniferous		Anaspidacea
	275	
Devonian		Earliest malacostracan—*Nahecaris.*
		Lepidocaris Conchostraca
Silurian		
	340	
Ordovician		Ostracods
	390	
Cambrian		? Ostracods Burgess Shales
		Pseudocrustacea
	450	? Conchostraca Trilobites

are squat and flattened, looking like minute isopods, and some have peculiarly developed limbs. Some harpacticids creep about on the surfaces of plants, others are semi-parasitic, but the majority live in mud or between sand grains.

This mode of life has been adopted by another smaller order, the Mystacocarida (fig. 8A). These have narrow bodies like some of the harpacticids, but the limbs are very different so that they are regarded as a separate group.

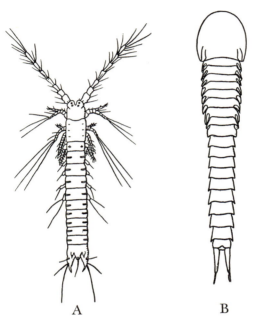

A   B

FIG. 8. A, *Derocheilocaris remanei* (Mystacocarida). Adult female, dorsal view. Actual length about 0.38 mm. (After Noodt, 1954). B, *Hutchinsoniella macra-cantha* (Cephalocarida) Dorsal view, the limbs are hidden by the body. The setae on the caudal rami extend to about half the length of the body. Actual length of body about 2.8 mm. (After Sanders, 1955).

A totally different way of life has been taken up by the cirripedes. The adult barnacles live attached to rocks and various other objects, and their whole anatomy has become modified to this end. The relation between the anatomy of a stalked barnacle, such as *Lepas*, and the anatomy of a more normal crustacean is illustrated in fig. 9, which has been adapted from the ingenious figure given by

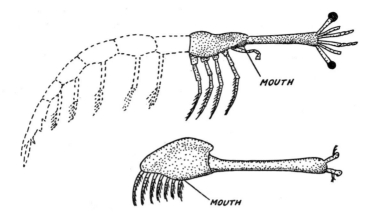

FIG. 9. Darwin's diagram of the relation between the anatomy of a stalked barnacle (*Lepas*) and a prawn (*Lucifer*). An important feature to note is that in *Lucifer* the preoral part of the head is elongated. Actually this comparison is superficial, because in the barnacle the internal organs become reorganised so that the ovary lies in the stalk.

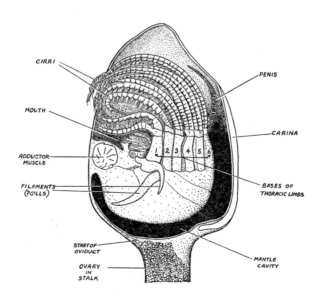

FIG. 10. *Lepas australis* (Cirripedia), with the right half of the mantle removed. The actual length of the part shown is about 2 cm.; the stalk extends to about 5 cm.

Darwin. The barnacle must be visualised as standing on its head, attached by cement made in a gland which opens on the antennule. The abdomen is reduced to a vestige, and the carapace encloses the whole body. The carapace of the cirripedes is usually called the mantle, this is a term which dates from the time when barnacles were thought to be molluscs. Various parts of the mantle are thickened and have calcium salts deposited in them to form definite plates. The number and arrangement of these plates are used to distinguish the various families and genera of barnacles.

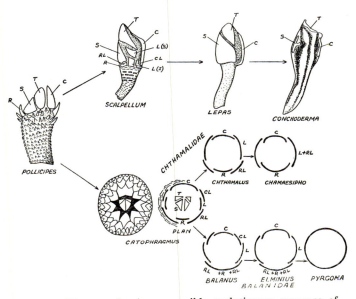

Fig. 11. Diagram showing a possible evolutionary sequence of some barnacles (Cirripedia) and the disposition of the plates. C=carina; CL=carino-lateral; L=lateral; L(I)=inferior lateral; L(S)=superior lateral; R=rostrum; RL=rostro-lateral; S= scutum; T=tergum. In the plan of *Catophragmus* the scales on the right side have been omitted. The scuta and terga have been omitted from the other plans.

It is thought that the regular arrangement of plates on the mantle has evolved from a system of more numerous, less regular plates. *Pollicipes* (fig. 11) is a primitive genus, dating from the Jurassic (150 million years ago), but still surviving to-day. A series can be traced from *Pollicipes*, through *Scalpellum* to *Lepas*, in which the scales on the stalk are reduced and the plates on the mantle become more regular. Some other stalked barnacles lose the mantle plates completely. A second line of evolution can be traced which involves the loss of the stalk to form acorn barnacles. *Catophragmus* is a stage which might be reached by reducing the stalk of *Pollicipes*; eight large plates are surrounded by a series of smaller scales. From a form with eight plates one can derive various others by the loss of some plates and the joining of other plates (fig. 11). Some cirripedes have became parasites; these are dealt with in chapter 8.

The various groups that have been dealt with so far have varied greatly in the number of segments constituting the body. In the

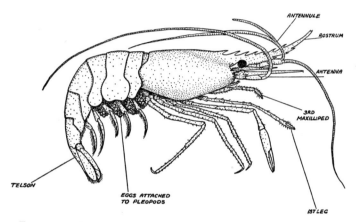

FIG. 12. *Palaemon* (=*Leander*) *serratus* (Decapoda Natantia). Adult female viewed from the right side. Actual length, from eye to tip of telson about 6 cm.

Malacostraca the segmentation has settled down, and the various segments can be aligned with one another throughout the mala-costracan orders. There are eight thoracic and seven abdominal segments, though as a rule only six abdominal segments are in evidence. It is a general rule that the male ducts open on the last thoracic segment and the female ducts open on the sixth thoracic segment. Within the limitations of this basic plan there has been great radiation into different groups, and a general increase in body size when compared with other Crustacea, so that the Malacostraca are now abundant, widespread and quite the most conspicuous of all the Crustacea.

The primary branchings in the radiation of the Malacostraca

are shown in fig. 13. Fossils which look very like some of the Leptostraca are known from the Devonian (about 300 million years ago), and some which bear a less marked resemblance date from even earlier periods. These fossils had a well developed carapace just like the modern forms, and had a telson bearing paired rami. The possession of these rami distinguishes the Leptostraca from all other Malacostraca. The thoracic limbs are also very peculiar in structure (fig. 22), quite different from those of other malacostracans, yet they are thought to represent a modification of a typical branched limb which has been altered by the animal adopting mud burrowing habits while retaining a filter feeding mechanism (p. 31).

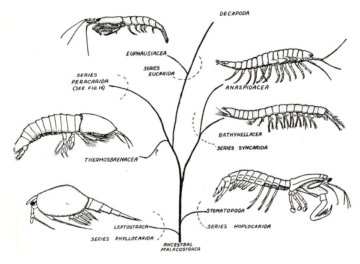

Fig 13. An evolutionary tree of the Malacostraca. Based on the ideas of Siewing (1956).

Another group with early fossil relatives is the order Anaspidacea. These are nowadays confined to Tasmania and south-eastern Australia, but fossils which agree in general body form and in details of limb structure are known from the Coal Measures of North America and Europe. They also have some more widespread minute relatives, the Bathynellacea, which are only about a milli-metre long and live in underground waters in various parts of the world (p. 142). They agree with the anaspids in lacking a carapace, and in not having a brood pouch under the thorax, as well as in other more technical details.

The presence, in the adult female, of a brood pouch under the
thorax is the hall-mark of the Peracarida, various members of
which are shown in fig. 14. A well-developed carapace is present
in the Mysidacea, and a less well-developed one in the Cumacea,
Tanaidacea and Spelaeogriphacea. In the last group the carapace
only covers the first thoracic segment; in the tanaids it is joined to
the first two thoracic segments, while in the Cumacea it is joined to
the first three or four segments of the thorax. The isopods and
amphipods do not have a carapace. It is in these two groups that
the greatest radiation has occurred. As a general rule it may be

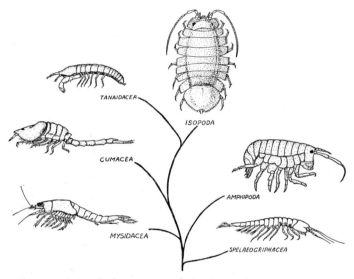

FIG. 14. An evolutionary tree of the Peracarida. Based on the
ideas of Siewing as modified by Gordon (1957).

said that the amphipods are flattened from side to side while the
isopods have flat backs, but there are various exceptions to this
rule. The best way of separating the two groups is to examine
the structure of the abdominal appendages. In the isopods they are
flattened and used for respiration, while in the amphipods they
are usually narrow and branched.

The question mark by the line leading to the Thermosbaenacea
in fig. 13 draws attention to the uncertainty of the systematic
position of these small creatures. Their anatomy is peculiar in

having a brood pouch formed by the carapace on the back of the female; no other malacostracan has a structure like this.

At one time zoologists included the Euphausiacea and the Mysidacea in a group called the Schizopoda, because the thoracic legs are branched. However, the euphausids do not have a brood pouch and so cannot be included in the Peracarida. They are very shrimp-like, but differ from the decapod shrimps in not having the first three pairs of thoracic limbs modified to form accessory mouth-parts or maxillipeds.

In many accounts of the Crustacea the Stomatopoda are left until the end, as if they were a further advance on the decapods, but this is by no means so. They have some primitive anatomical features, such as four free thoracic segments not covered by the carapace, and a long tubular heart. Their peculiarities include the highly modified second thoracic limbs which resemble the front legs of a praying mantis, and they have two freely articulated segments in the head which bear the eyes and the antennules. In spite of their superficial resemblance to lobsters the Mantis Shrimps are a peculiar and quite isolated group of the Malacostraca.

The name Decapoda implies the presence of ten legs, and this is true of most decapods, though the legs are not always large and functional. The first three pairs of thoracic limbs are modified as mouthparts (maxillipeds) and help in the feeding mechanism, while the remaining five pairs of thoracic limbs are leg-like. The first pair of these legs usually bears a pair of pincers or chelae which are used to catch food and for defence.

In many ways the decapods are a most satisfactory group to study from an evolutionary point of view, because the way in which one type of organisation has arisen from another can easily be visualised, and various types are in existence showing inter-mediate stages. The type of organisation referred to is of course the crab type, with its broad carapace and the abdomen tucked forwards underneath. The way in which this type has arisen from a creature like a lobster is not difficult to visualise when one looks at *Galathea* and various other anomurans, even though these creatures may not actually be intermediates in the line of descent.

A primary division of the Decapoda can be made to give the sub orders Natantia, the swimmers, and Reptantia, the crawlers. This is not to say that some of the Reptantia do not swim—in fact several of them do. The distinguishing feature is the method of swimming. The Natantia use the abdominal appendages (pleopods) which are large and 'feathered' for this purpose, while those members of the Reptantia which swim do so without using their pleopods.

The Natantia include the prawns and shrimps, but it should be made clear that these popular names have no scientific application; they are applied indiscriminately to various members of the sub-order. In common English usage shrimp is usually applied to members of the genus *Crangon*, the pink shrimp is *Pandalus montagui*, and the name prawn is given to members of the genus *Palaemon*. In North America members of the last genus are called shrimps.

Three groups can be distinguished within the Natantia. These are the Penaeidea, with the first three pairs of legs bearing pincers, the Stenopodidea, also with three pairs of pincers, but with the third legs stronger than the first two, and the Caridea, which have no pincers on the third legs. The Penaeidea are regarded as the most primitive of these groups, and they are among the earliest fossil decapods, being found in the Triassic deposits of Madagascar. The Caridea are not found until the Jurassic period, while the Steno-podidea are not known as fossils, probably because they are delicate and not easily preserved.

The really big Crustacea belong to the Reptantia. Lobsters (*Homarus* species) sometimes reach a weight of nearly forty pounds, and there is a giant Japanese spider crab (*Macrocheira kaempferi*) with legs spanning eight feet.

Dividing the Reptantia into sub groups is a troublesome business, because intermediates between the various proposed groups are common, and much depends on which structures one thinks are important. For our purpose we can divide the group into the usual four sub groups: the Palinura, Astacura, Anomura and Brachyura. The first two are sometimes grouped together as the Macrura, the big tails, but this is also a term which is sometimes applied to these together with the Natantia, so that its use is generally to be avoided, although sometimes useful as a descriptive term.

The Palinura differ from the true lobsters and crayfish (Astacura) in not having a pointed rostrum and in lacking the characteristically enlarged pincers. The spiny lobsters, *Palinurus* and *Panulirus*, reach a considerable size; there is an authentic record of an American species reaching a weight of 26 pounds, and an uncon-firmed record of one weighing 34 pounds.

True crabs, or Brachyura, are the most numerous members of

the Reptantia, with over 4,400 species spread throughout the world. They are characterised by the small abdomen tucked forwards under the body, and by the lack of a tail fan. One group, the Dromiacea, still has remants of a tail fan, and is regarded as the most primitive group of the Brachyura. This opinion is supported by the fossil record; the Dromiacea were the dominant crabs during the Jurassic, before other crabs had evolved. Some authorities regard the Dromiacea as too primitive to be included in the Brachyura and would put them in a group on their own.

The Anomura show many features which are intermediate between those of true crabs and lobsters, as well as having their own specialisations. Some, such as *Galathea* (fig. 15) carry the abdomen flexed forwards beneath the thorax, but it is still capable

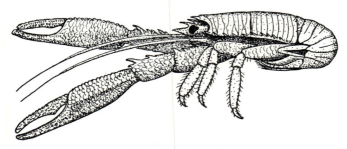

Fig. 15. *Galathea squamifera* (Decapoda, Reptantia), an anomuran
Notice the small last leg tucked in between the abdomen and the
thorax. Actual length of body in position shown about 3 cm.

of complete extension backwards. The hermit crabs have large soft abdomens which they keep covered with the empty shells of various molluscs. In connection with this peculiar habit they have lost the appendages on the right side of the abdomen. This anatomical peculiarity gives a clue to the ancestry of the Robber Crab, *Birgus latro*, which has a hard symmetrical abdomen, but only has pleopods on the left side. The most reasonable explanation is that the Robber Crab has descended from hermit crabs which gave up carrying shells and redeveloped a hard abdomen, but could not regain their lost appendages.

Some of the Anomura, such as the porcelain crabs (family Porcellanidae), look like true crabs, but the small abdomen has a distinct tail fan, and the last pair of legs are small and tucked into the space between the carapace and the abdomen, leaving the

c

crab with only three pairs of effective walking legs apart from the pincers.

To summarise the course that the evolution of the Crustacea has taken it may be said that they probably began as small creatures possessing many of the characters of the Branchiopoda. The actual origin of the Crustacea is obscure; they clearly originated early in the fossil record, but there is no definite evidence about their ancestors. The limbs and general organisation of the head of the primitive Crustacea are quite different from those of the trilobites, and it is probable that the latter group represents a quite separate line of evolution.

After a period of experimentation, involving variation in the number of segments in the body, and the radiation of small species into a wide range of habitats, the basic malacostracan plan produced a highly successful group of larger creatures, culminating in the evolution of the Decapoda and the production of the crabs.

LITERATURE

CALMAN, W. T. (1909). Crustacea. In *Treatise of Zoology*, Pt. 7, ed. E. R. Lankester. London.

DARWIN, C. (1851). A monograph of the Cirripedia. 2 vols. Ray Society. London.

GORDON, I. (1957). On *Spelaeogriphus*, a new cavernicolous crustacean from South Africa. *Bull. Brit. Mus. (Nat. Hist.)* 5: 29-47.

SANDERS, H. L. (1957). The Cephalocarida and crustacean phylogeny. *Syst. Zool.* 6: 112-129.

SCOURFIELD, D. J. (1926). On a new type of crustacean from the Old Red Sandstone (Rhynie chert bed, Aberdeenshire)—*Lepidocaris rhyniensis*, gen. et sp. nov. *Phil. Trans.* B. 214: 153-187.

SIEWING, R. (1956). Untersuchungen zur Morphologie der Malacostraca (Crustacea). *Zool. Jahrb. (Anat.)* 75: 39-176.

TIEGS, O. W., & MANTON, S. M. (1958). The evolution of the Arthropoda. *Biol. Rev.* 33: 255-337.

CHAPTER II

FEEDING, LOCOMOTION
AND RESPIRATION

T H I S chapter is really a continuation of the last, because the three activities forming its subject are those which have become diversified and whose requirements govern the shapes assumed by various crustaceans. Of the three processes, feeding has become the most varied, and to a large extent the evolution of the Crustacea has been the evolution of their feeding methods.

It is now generally accepted that the primitive mode of feeding in the Crustacea is by means of water currents from which small particles are filtered off. The process of gathering small particles may be divided into three stages: the production of feeding currents, separation of particles from the currents, and transport of particles to the mouth. The methods used to perform these processes are best illustrated by considering two examples in some detail, and then discussing the variations found in other groups. The Anostraca have been chosen as one group because their feeding mechanism shows certain characteristics which are present in the feeding mechanisms of other Branchiopoda. The Mysidacea are chosen as the second example because their feeding mechanism can be considered as the primitive type in the Malacostraca.

In the Anostraca the water currents are produced by the beating of the thoracic limbs. The same movements serve to propel the creature through the water and to gather its food. The limbs do not all move in unison; one limb is usually about one-sixth of a complete beat ahead of the limb in front of it. The beating of the limbs alternately enlarges and reduces the space between two successive limbs, so sucking water in and blowing it out again. The limbs are arranged so that the water enters the interlimb spaces from the median space which lies in the midline between the two rows of limbs. Water must then flow into the median space to replace that which has entered the interlimb spaces. This current flowing into the median space is the feeding current. Small particles are swept into the median space, and are prevented from leaving

by the fine setae which project backwards from the inner edges of
the limbs to form a strainer between the median space and the
interlimb spaces. The main filtering region is near the bases of the
limbs where the flow into the interlimb spaces is greatest.

During the backstroke (towards the tail) water is pressed out of
the interlimb spaces; much escapes via the tips and outer edges,
providing the thrust which propels the animal through the water.
Some water is also forced back into the median space, blowing
food particles off the setae. At the end of a backstroke two successive limbs become pressed closely together, because the rear limb
starts its forward stroke while the front limb is still moving back-

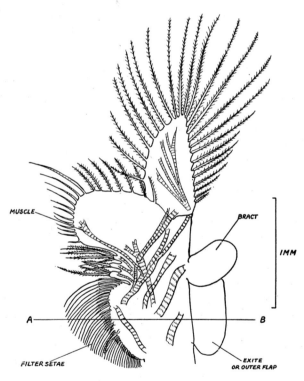

Fig. 16. Trunk limb of *Artemia salina* (Anostraca). The
limb is shown as it appears when flattened, but in life
it is bent as shown in the section in fig. 17. Note the
numerous intrinsic muscles which can alter the shape of
the limb. The detailed structure of the filter setae is too
fine to be shown. The line A-B gives the approximate
level of the section shown in fig. 17.

wards; this results in further extrusion of water from the inter-limb space. Now the limbs are not just simple flaps, but are thicker along the middle of their length than near the inner and outer edges. This means that when the limbs are pressed close together the inter-limb space is divided into two parts, and water can only escape from the inner part by going back into the median space. There is a small, forwardly directed groove near the base of each limb which allows water to escape from the inner part of the inter-limb space. The spurt of water at the end of a backstroke thus blows food particles in the basal part of the food groove towards the mouth.

Food particles are also removed from the filter setae by another method. As two successive limbs move forwards the setae of the front limb will be sucked back against the inner edge of the limb behind and against the body wall at the base of that limb. Both the inner edge of the limb and the body wall at its base are provided with fine setae which project between the filter setae of the limb in front and comb food particles into the median space, where they can be blown towards the mouth by the spurts of water from the inner parts of the interlimb spaces at the end of a backstroke.

Food is moved forwards in the midline until it reaches the level of the second maxillae, where it becomes entangled in a secretion from the large glands in the labrum. The maxillules push the sticky mass into the mouth.

The important features to note about the anostracan method of feeding are: (1) all the thoracic limbs are involved in both swimming and feeding, (2) food is passed forwards in the midline between the limbs, and (3) there is a large labrum which secretes a viscous fluid to consolidate the food before it is swallowed.

Feeding and locomotion have become separated in the Conchostraca. The feeding mechanism is similar in its basic feature to that of the Anostraca, but the limbs are enclosed in a carapace, and the current flowing out from the inter-limb spaces cannot be used for swimming. The branched antennae take over this function, and have well-developed muscles which are not present in the Anostraca. A further complication in the Conchostraca is that some of the hind limbs do not act as filters, but have strong spines on the inner sides of their bases. These spiny bases can act as jaws and break up larger food particles than can be collected by the normal filtering mechanism. As these larger particles are broken up they are passed slowly forwards from the base of one limb to the base of the limb in front. By the time the particles reach the front filtering limbs they are finely divided enough to be collected in the normal filtering mechanism and passed forwards to the mouth by spurts of water from the inter-limb spaces. The Conchostraca thus chew with their hind limbs and filter with their front limbs.

The process of taking in large particles for chewing by the hind limbs leads to a danger of blocking the median space. If this happens the offending particle can be removed by means of the

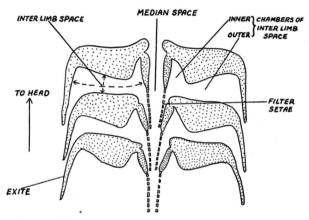

FIG. 17. Diagrammatic horizontal section through three successive limbs of an anostracan. Note that when the limbs move forwards towards the head each exite will press back against the limb behind and will prevent water from entering the interlimb space via the outer edge, but the exites will allow the exit of water from the interlimb space when the limbs are pressed together. (After Cannon, 1933).

claws on the end of the abdomen, which can be flexed forwards into the median space and then kicked violently backwards.

A similar kicking of the abdomen is seen in the Cladocera, which may be thought of as small Conchostraca with only a few limbs. They retain the filtering activities of the conchostracan front limbs but have lost the hind chewing limbs. The actual number of filtering limbs is reduced to four in *Sida* and only two in *Daphnia*. Some of the Chydoridae do not filter small particles out of currents, but apply their limbs closely to the surfaces of plants and scrape particles off. *Anchistropus* feeds in the same manner on the common brown *Hydra,* and has a specially modified claw on the first pair of legs for holding on to its victim. A more active predatory mode of life has been adopted by *Leptodora* and *Bythotrephes*; in these genera the limbs have lost the filtering mechanism altogether and have become modified for grasping.

The Notostraca feed on larger particles than most other Branchiopoda. Moderate sized particles are passed backwards by the tips of the beating limbs, and as the food travels backwards it is gradually brought nearer to the body, so that when it reaches the hind limbs it is down between their bases. The hind limb bases

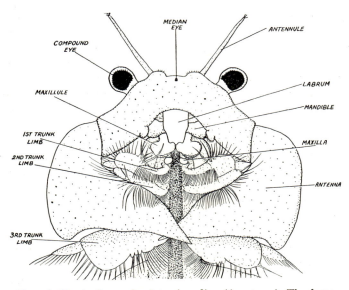

FIG. 18. Head of a male *Artemia salina* (Anostraca). The large antennae are used to clasp the females. Note the forwardly directed spines on the maxillae, and the way in which the labrum overlaps the mandibles. Notice also the way in which the filter setae form walls to the median space between the two rows of limbs.

break up the food to some extent—a feature reminiscent of the Conchostraca, and it is then passed forwards by the spiny inward projecting bases of the limbs. Each inward projection passes the food to the limb in front, and so ultimately to the mouth. There are no water currents of the type found in the Anostraca, and true filtratory setae are absent. Large food masses are sometimes held against the mouthparts by the front limbs and bitten into by the spiny bases of these limbs and the first maxillae. In spite of the differences from other branchiopods there is a basic resemblance in the fact that all the limbs play a part in the collection of food and that this food is ultimately passed forwards from the hind limbs towards the mouth.

The beating of the notostracan limbs provides the swimming current as well as the feeding mechanism, and is thus comparable with the anostracan limb beat. The notostracan carapace does not extend around the limbs and interfere with the swimming current as it does in the Conchostraca and Cladocera, which have to use their antennae for swimming. Respiratory exchange is assumed to be through the general surface of the body, but there is some evidence that the epipodites, or bracts (see fig. 16) of the Branchiopoda are more permeable than the rest of the body, and there may be more exchange here than elsewhere, particularly as the bracts are subjected to a constant flow of water over their surfaces.

A rather different method of feeding which involves all the thoracic limbs is that found in the barnacles. The thoracic legs take the form of branched cirri, beset with fine setae, and are arranged in such a way that they all curl forwards, with the fine setae forming a net. This net is pushed out of the opening of the mantle and then moved forwards and downwards towards the mouth. During the forward movement the cirri are spread wide apart and then brought closer together as they move downwards. The whole movement resembles a many fingered hand grasping through the water. Small particles in the water near the barnacle are caught and swept towards the mouth. When a barnacle is feeding vigorously the thorax moves up and down inside the mantle, and a current of water flows in over the front edge of the shell and comes out as a spurt behind the thorax as it descends. This flow of water through the mantle cavity is obviously an advantage from the respiratory point of view, particularly when eggs are being kept in the mantle cavity prior to hatching. Sometimes a barnacle will pump water through its mantle cavity without extending its cirri into the water; movements of the thorax within the mantle are responsible for such respiratory movements without feeding. The actual rate of movement of the cirri during feeding varies with a number of factors. The age of the barnacle is important; as a rule older barnacles beat their cirri more slowly than young ones. Variation in rate of beating with temperature can be related to the geographical distribution of allied species. *Balanus amphitrite* lives in tropical and warm temperate regions, and has its maximum rate of beating at about 30° C., while *B. balanus*, a northern species, beats most rapidly at about 20° C. Type of habitat also has its effect, the highest rates of beating of *Balanus balanoides* has been found among specimens collected from high water level in a sheltered site without currents. This is perhaps what one might expect, because barnacles living in such a situation will only be covered by water for a short period, and they will not have the advantage of food being brought towards them by currents. It is noticeable that barnacles high on the shore do not grow as quickly as those lower down (see p. 67).

In the remaining groups of Crustacea we find that when a filtering method of feeding is used the filter is usually restricted to particular limbs, and that those nearer the mouth are generally of the greatest importance. In a filter-feeding ostracod, such as *Asterope*, the filter is borne on the maxillule (1st maxilla) and a water current is caused to flow in at the front of the shell and out at the back, by the beating of a flap on the second maxilla. The small particles which collect on the filter are scraped off by setae which project forwards from the second maxilla, and by others which project back from the base of the mandible. These setae pass food to another group of setae which project from the base of the maxillule towards the mouth, and finally the food is pushed into the oesophagus by long processes on the bases of the mandibles. Not all ostracods feed in this way. Another filter-feeder, *Cytherella*, has a filter on the mandible, and the water current is produced by the beating of a flap on the maxillule as well as the second maxilla. Yet other ostracods are predators and catch copepods, or even mysids.

Among the copepods we find that many of the Calanoida are filter-feeders. The filter is borne on the second maxilla, and trapped food particles are swept towards the mouth by setae on the first maxilla. The food of *Calanus finmarchicus* consists to a large extent of diatoms, but some Crustacea are also included in the diet, and it is thought that these must be caught by individual acts of capture, rather than by the filtering mechanism.

The ability to capture other creatures is probably primitive among the Copepoda. The Centropagidae, which can be regarded as the most primitive family of the Calanoida, feed mainly on other creatures which they capture, or on large particles of detritus.

Calanoids swim in two distinct ways. They have a slow gliding movement brought about by rotatory movement of the antennae,

mandibular palps and the first maxilla, and they can move in a
series of rapid jerks brought about by all the limbs and the
abdomen with its caudal rami. The latter movement is usually used
as an escape mechanism, or sometimes as a means of surprising
prey. A few species, such as *Anomalocera patersoni*, can move with
such vigour that they can hurl themselves right out of the water,
and a shoal of these creatures can appear like a rain shower on
the surface of the sea. Another species, *Pontellina mediterranea*,
has been described as 'taking long flying leaps out of the water,
after the manner of a flying fish'. If this is really so it is the only
case of aerial locomotion among the Crustacea, apart from an
unconfirmed report of a large flying malacostracan sighted off the
Phillipine Islands.

Some of the cyclopoid copepods are also predators. Species such
as *Macrocyclops albidus* seize their prey with the first maxillae
and hold it while the other mouthparts dismember it and push
it into the mouth. Other members of the Cyclopoida are herbivores
and feed on diatoms or small filamentous algae.

The feeding habits of the harpacticid copepods are not well
known. Many of them appear to be detritus feeders; they creep
about between sand grains and undulate their bodies in a characteristic manner. Others are known which feed, at least in their young
stages, on algae. *Thalestris rhodymeniae* has nauplii which live in
mines or galleries inside the red alga *Rhodymenia palmata*, and
the nauplii of *Dactylopusioides macrolabris* live in similar mines
in the brown alga *Dictyota dichotoma*. The nauplii of both these
species are remarkable for the great development of the base of the
antenna, which bears a cutting edge and functions like a mandible,
while the true mandible appears to be incapable of biting. These
miners in the fronds of seaweeds are an interesting parallel to the
insect leaf miners of land plants.

The feeding mechanism of the Cephalocarida has not yet been
described, but the Mystacocarida are said to be filterers, and the
filters are located in the maxillary region. This would agree with
their being placed somewhere near the copepods in the scheme of
classification.

The original feeding mechanism of the Malacostraca is also
thought to be of the filtering type. The basic mechanism consists
of a filter on the inner border of the second maxilla. A water
current is made to flow through the filter, from behind, by the
vibration of the maxilla itself. The base of the first thoracic limb

bears a group of brush-like setae which push the food trapped on the filter forwards to the maxillules where another group of setae pushes the food on to the mandibles, and so into the mouth. A mechanism of this type is found in the mysidacean *Gnathophausia*, which is a primitive representative of its group. *Gnathophausia* swims by means of its abdominal limbs (pleopods), and uses the

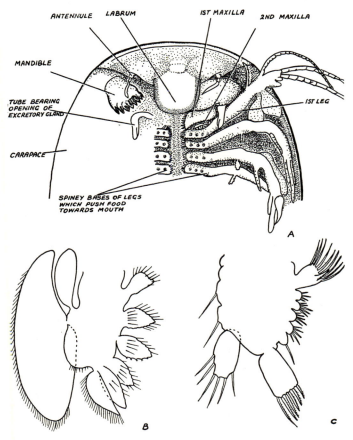

FIG. 19. A, Head of *Triops granarius* (Notostraca). The legs on the left side of the figure have been omitted, and the mandible on that side pulled back to show its teeth, which are normally hidden beneath the labrum. Notice that there are no antennae, the functions of these organs are taken over by the prolongations from the first leg. B, Trunk limb of *Triops granarius*, note the absence of filter setae. C, Second trunk limb of *Lepidocaris*, orientated in the same way as fig. B, with the inner border to the right (C, after Scourfield, 1926).

currents produced by its thoracic limbs for respiratory purposes. The outer branches (exopods) of the thoracic limbs are held out sideways from the body and each one is rotated in such a manner as to produce a vortex with its centre along the centre about which the limb rotates. Water swirls up the vortex and bathes the gills which lie at the bases of the legs, those of one side meeting those of the other in the midline.

In some other mysids, such as *Hemimysis*, the pleopods are reduced and the thoracic limbs have taken over the function of locomotion, and, further, they produce an auxiliary feeding current. Again the exopods produce a vortex and water swirls up from the tip of the limb towards the body (fig. 20B). Now *Hemimysis* does not have gills, so that a clear space, or groove, is left along the midline, between the two rows of limbs. Water from the two sides of the body meets in the midline and passes forwards, partly due to the forward inclination of the opening at the bases of the legs and partly due to suction resulting from movements of the second maxilla. The food particles carried along by these currents are trapped on the filter setae of the second maxillae and so enter the basic feeding mechanism already described.

Gnathophausia and *Hemimysis* are not restricted to feeding on small particles; they can eat large particles when the need arises. The inner branches (endopods) of the thoracic limbs hold large particles against the mandibles, which bite into the food material and pass it upwards into the oesophagus.

The rotation of the thoracic exopods also propels *Hemimysis* through the water. This is done by virtue of the arrangement of the setae at the tips of the exopod, which are arranged so that they spread out and offer great resistance to the water as the exopod moves backwards, but close together and offer minimal resistance as the exopod moves forwards. A special respiratory current is produced by a small flap at the base of the first leg. This flap, or epipodite, projects into the space between the body and the carapace, and by its movements it draws water in under the dorsal hind edge of the carapace, and pushes it out at the sides of the two pairs of maxillae. *Hemimysis* does not have special gills, but the carapace is richly supplied with blood spaces, which bring the blood into close contact with the respiratory current. As the respiratory current leaves the sides of the maxillae it gets swept upwards behind the eye (fig. 20A) and then backwards with the main swimming current.

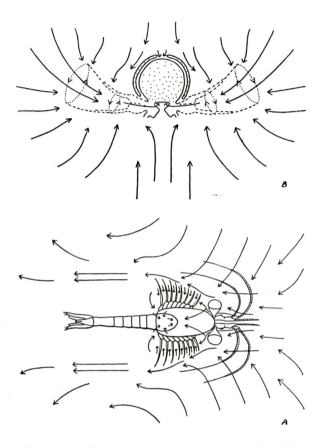

FIG. 20. Feeding and swimming currents produced by *Hemimysis lamornae* (Mysidacea). A, Dorsal view showing the currents produced as the animal swims through the water. Note the large backwardly directed locomotory current, the smaller current down to the bases of the legs, the inhalent respiratory current under the hind edge of the carapace, and the exhalent respiratory current coming up behind the eyes.   B, Diagram of a transverse section of one thoracic segment and its legs showing the vortex produced by rotation of the exopodite and the water entering the median food groove. The endopodite of each leg has been omitted. (After Cannon and Manton, 1927).

Some members of the Mysidacea have lost the ability to filter feed. This is so with *Lophogaster typicus*, which lives on muddy patches of the sea floor, and feeds on large pieces of food, which it holds in the same way as *Hemimysis* when it feeds on such particles. The respiratory current is similar to that of *Gnatho-phausia*, but the gills are larger and smoother, probably because of the creature's mud-dwelling habits. The increased size will compensate to some extent for the poor aeration of the water, and the smoothness helps to prevent the gills from becoming clogged by the particles of mud.

Mud dwelling has been adopted as a way of life by various other Crustacea, including the Leptostraca and the Cumacea. Both these groups contain filter-feeders, but the mechanisms differ from each other and from that found in the mysids, nevertheless certain resemblances between the three types can be traced.

In the cumacean *Diastylis* the second maxilla is still the bearer of the filter setae, but the current which flows through these setae is produced by the action of a large epipodite on the first thoracic limb. The water current, which also serves as a respiratory current, is unusual in that it enters the carapace from in front and also leaves from the front, though a little higher up than the site of intake (fig. 21). The leptostracan *Nebalia bipes* has adopted a different method of filter-feeding, which at first sight resembles a return to the

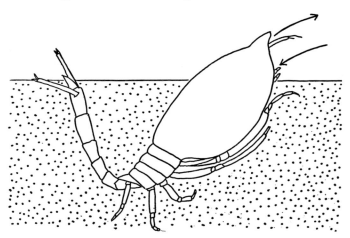

Fig. 21. *Diastylis* sp. (Cumacea) buried in sand, showing the inhalent and exhalent feeding and respiratory currents. (After Dennel, 1937).

anostracan method of feeding, but there are certain fundamental differences. It is true that the filters are carried on the inner borders of the thoracic limbs and that food is trapped in the median space between the two rows of limbs. But there the resemblance ends. The legs are arranged so that when they move they suck in water from in front of the animal and pass it out backwards. Food trapped by the filter setae is passed forwards by groups of brush-like setae which project from one limb to the next in front, and as the limbs move in relation to each other the food is transferred towards the mouth (fig. 22).

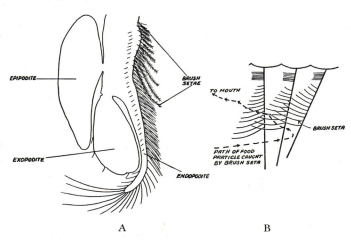

A   B

FIG. 22. A, Trunk limb of *Nebalia* (Leptostraca). The brush setae project obliquely forwards from the inner margin of the limb. B, Diagram showing the way in which the brush setae move food particles forwards towards the mouth. (B, after Cannon, 1927).

Larger particles are trapped before they enter the space between the limbs and are bitten into by the spiny bases of the maxillules. When a large mass accumulates near the maxillules the palps of the mandibles can be bent backwards and push the food into the mouth to be subjected to the crushing action of the main body of the mandible.

A further complication is found in the deep water plankton form *Nebaliopsis*, which is regarded as a more specialised relative of *Nebalia*. The thoracic limbs of *Nebaliopsis* appear to produce a current in the opposite direction from that produced by *Nebalia*. This has been deduced from a study of preserved specimens, but the analysis seems quite reasonable. The current flows forwards, and food particles are trapped in the midline between the legs, but there is also a filter on the first thoracic leg and the second maxilla. It looks as if *Nebaliopsis* has regained a maxillary filter after its ancestors had lost it, but in reality the filter on the maxilla of *Nebaliopsis* acts in combination with a filter on the first leg, and so is quite different from the primitive malacostracan type. Further, this filter is probably cleared and the food passed to the mouth by the action of the mandibular palps. The sequence of the evolution of *Nebaliopsis*, as visualised by Cannon, is as follows. Certain mysid-like creatures took to burrowing in mud, gave up swimming and developed a large carapace which protected their gills from the clogging effect of their environment. The maxillary filter was lost because it became clogged too quickly, and the animals fed on large particles. They took to moving about in the mud by an oar-like action of the antennules, which tended to suck water into the front of the carapace. In this way an irregular water current was established and later reinforced and regularised by the action of the thoracic limbs, which became paddle-shaped. The increase in the stream entering the front of the carapace would bring in more food and many small particles which were eventually collected when a new filter mechanism developed on the thoracic legs. This brings us to a creature like *Nebalia*. It is then thought that some of these creatures gave up living in mud and started to swim in the plankton. This was accompanied by a redevelopment of a filter near to the mouth, which was not now in danger of clogging, and a widening of the carapace, so that water was sucked in from all directions. Later it stopped being drawn in from in front, and a stage similar to *Nebaliopsis* was reached.

Further work has shown that *Nebaliopsis typica* has an enormous sac opening into its gut, and that the gut is modified for sucking. It is now thought that *N. typica* is an egg sucker. The scarcity of eggs in deep water makes it necessary for *Nebaliopsis* to take as many eggs as possible when they are available—hence the enormous sac for storage. This does not deny the possibility that the filter may also be useful to tide the animal over periods when eggs are not available.

The scheme of evolution which has just been described gives an idea of the complexity of the path that evolution has taken within the Crustacea. The story becomes more complicated when we turn to other groups of the Malacostraca.

The evolutionary trend from the Mysidacea towards the Isopoda has passed somewhere near the Tanaidacea, some of which still have a maxillary filter, but it seems to be of minor importance to them, and they feed mainly on large particles. Most of the isopods and amphipods have biting mouthparts; the maxillules often have strong sharp spines which help to break up the food, and one or more pairs of legs may be subchelate. This modification is useful for holding food against the mouthparts while pieces are being broken off. Some species, such as the isopod *Mesidotea entomon* use the subchelate thoracic legs to catch small animals, and can manipulate their prey with considerable dexterity.

The caprellids (fig. 23) are usually found attached to small colonial coelenterates, and it used to be thought that they fed on the small polyps, but they have been observed to catch copepods as

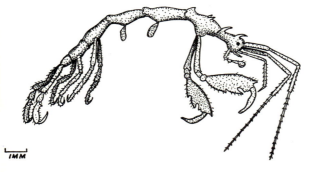

Fig. 23. *Pseudoprotella phasma.* (Amphipoda, Caprellidea) lateral view of male

they swim by. The caprellid has a sense organ in its antennule which is sensitive to small water currents. When a movement is perceived the caprellid turns towards it with its large subchelate second leg held in a ready position. The actual catching of the prey is done with the large subchela and is probably dependant on the prey being sighted. Once caught the prey is held in front of the mouthparts and small pieces are torn off by the small first pair of subchelae and pushed into the mouth.

One general feature to be noticed in the amphipods and isopods is that the thoracic legs are not used for swimming. They have become true walking legs, and swimming, when done, is performed by means of the pleopods on the abdomen. In the Isopoda the pleopods are also respiratory organs and are flattened for this purpose, but the amphipods have special flaps, on the inner sides

D

of their thoracic limbs, which appear to serve as respiratory surfaces.

A return to filter-feeding has been made by the amphipod *Haustorius arenarius*. This species lives in sand containing a fair amount of organic detritus. The filter is made up of the usual setae, and is situated on the second maxilla, but it is not the same as the original mysid filter. The water current is produced by a rotatory movement of the second maxilla, and the food sieved out of the current is removed by a comb-like series of setae on the first thoracic limb, which is so modified that it is considered as one of the mouthparts and is called the maxilliped. An important differ-ence from the mysid is that the palp of the maxilliped bears the comb which removes food from the filter; in the mysid the work is done by a group of setae at the base of the limb. The palp of the maxilliped passes the food forwards, around the second maxillae to the maxillules, which in turn pass it to the mandibles and so into the mouth.

It is interesting to note that in the two examples of redevelopment of a filter mechanism that we have studied the organ removing trapped food from the filter is a palp: In *Nebalia* and *Nebaliopsis* it is the mandibular palp, and in *Haustorius* the maxillipedal palp. Palps are highly mobile structures, and are usually well provided with setae, so that the development of a brush on some part of them does not present any great difficulty. The mobility of the palps may well confer advantages which are denied to a brush situated in the primitive position at the base of a limb.

In the decapods the three front thoracic legs have become modified to form maxillipeds; they help in the general dismember-ing and passing of food into the mouth. Swimming, in the adult stage, is performed by the movements of the pleopods in shrimps and prawns, or by movement of the last thoracic legs in the swim-ming crabs (fig. 24). Walking is the main function of the thoracic legs, though the first pair behind the maxillipeds are modified to form the chelae, which are used to catch and hold food. The gills are housed in chambers on either side of the body, between the body and the carapace, and a current is caused to flow over them by the beating of a backwardly projecting process from the exopodite of the second maxilla. This process, or scaphognathite as it is called, causes water to flow into the gill chamber through small openings between the edge of the carapace and the bases of the legs. The current flows between the gills and then out through small openings near the bases of the antennae. The position of this outflow is helpful in removing the products of the excretory organ, which opens on the base of the antenna.

The surfaces of the gills are kept clean by the action of long processes (epipodites) extending backwards from the bases of the maxillipeds. These epipodites sweep over the gills and dislodge any particles which may have entered with the respiratory current. The current can also be reversed, so that water flows into the gill

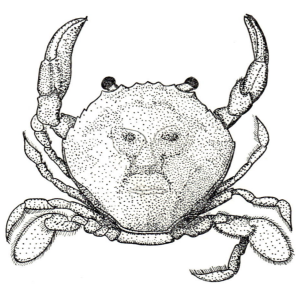

Fig. 24. *Polybius henslowi* (Decapoda, Brachyura), a swimming crab; note the large paddles at the ends of the last pair of legs. Although this crab is about the same size as the shore crab, *Carcinus,* its exoskeleton is much thinner and lighter. Actual width of carapace about 5 cm.

chamber through the usual exit. This is a useful additional mechanism for clearing the gill chamber of foreign particles.

Some crabs make regular use of the reversed current. The masked crab, *Corystes cassivelaunus,* lives in fine sand, and buries itself below the surface. The antennae are long, and each bears two rows of setae which overlap those of the other antenna and form a tube leading to the sand surface. By using the reverse respiratory current water is drawn down through this tube and is passed out through the openings at the bases of the legs. A similar modification is found in the anomuran *Albunea,* but the tube is formed by the antennules, not by the antennae.

Another method of obtaining a clean respiratory current is found in the crab *Calappa,* which also burrows in sand. The chelae of this species are relatively enormous, but the biting part is comparatively small. At one time it was thought that *Calappa* used its chelae to hide its food from other crabs and fish while it was being dealt with by the mouthparts. They may in fact do this, but the other function which they perform is probably more important. The two chelae fit neatly together in front of the carapace, and also fit closely against the front edge of the carapace. The narrow gap between carapace and chelae is guarded by hairs on the edge of the carapace and spines on the chelae. Water is drawn in through this guarded crack, and the hairs prevent any stray particles from entering. The inflowing water enters the gill chambers via openings near the bases of the legs. The outflowing current is carried upwards by tubes formed from the inner branches of the first maxillipeds, and is thus directed away from the current going inwards between the carapace and the chelae.

The majority of the Decapoda Reptantia are predators and scavengers; they will eat practically anything of animal origin. Perhaps the most remarkable record is of North American crayfish entering dens of hibernating snakes and eating the reptiles which were too torpid to retaliate.

It might be thought that once the decapods had developed biting mouthparts and chelae for catching their prey they would be content, but a surprising number of species, particularly anomurans, have developed other methods of feeding, some of which represent a return to filtration.

The fiddler crabs of the genus *Uca* have one enormous chela, and one small one. The males use the large one for defence and display during courtship, but the small one is used to scoop up sand grains and present them to the mouthparts. The first and second maxillipeds have numerous stout setae, some shaped like spoons. These are used to scour the sand grains for traces of organic matter. The sand is then rejected, often in the form of neat sand balls.

Some species literally brush up their food from the surface of sand or mud. *Galathea dispersa* has a brush on the end of its third maxilliped, and the particles which collect on the brush as it sweeps across the surface of the sand are removed by the second maxillipeds which pass the food inwards to the mouth.

Yet another method is used by *Porcellana longicornis*, which has its third maxilliped fringed with long featherlike hairs which stand out to form a spoon-shaped scoop. The crab swings these scoops out sideways and spreads the setae out wide, then brings them smartly back towards the other mouthparts entangling any particles which happen to be suspended in the water. The second maxillipeds brush the entangled particles out of the scoop and pass them towards the mouth.

A return to the production of a water current which has to pass through a filter is made by *Upogebia pugattensis*. This species lives in burrows and it produces a water current by the beating of its pleopods. The filter is borne on the first trunk limb behind the maxillipeds. Food trapped on this filter is combed off by the third maxillipeds which in turn are cleaned by the second maxillipeds and so on towards the mouth.

The history of crustacean feeding mechanisms and attendant modifications of locomotion and respiration, as outlined above, has provided a complicated picture. The alternate losing and regaining of filtering mechanisms make it look as if the Crustacea could not make up their mind about which method of feeding they wanted to specialise in. They have however been most successful in feeding on both large and small particles, and the occasional return to filter feeding by a representative of a group which feeds predominantly on large particles is an indication of great ability to radiate and to utilise all the assets that the environment can provide, rather than of indecision about an evolutionary trend.

LITERATURE

CANNON, H. G. (1927). On the feeding mechanism of *Nebalia bipes*. *Trans. roy. Soc. Edinb.* 55: 355-369.

CANNON, H. G. (1928). On the feeding mechanism of the copepods, *Calanus finmarchicus* and *Diaptomus gracilis*. *Brit. J. exp. Biol.* 6: 131-144.

CANNON, H. G. (1933). On the feeding mechanisms of certain marine ostracods. *Trans. roy. Soc. Edinb.* 57: 739-764.

CANNON, H. G. (1933). On the feeding mechanism of the Branchiopoda. *Phil. Trans.* B. 222: 267-352.

CANNON, H. G. (1946). *Nebaliopsis typica*. Discovery Repts. 23: 213-222.

38   A BIOLOGY OF CRUSTACEA

CANNON, H. G., & MANTON, S. M. (1927). On the feeding mechanism of a mysid crustacean, *Hemimysis lamornae*. *Trans. roy. Soc. Edinb.* 55: 219-253.

DENNELL, R. (1933). The habits and feeding mechanism of the amphipod *Haustorius arenarius* Slabber. *J. Linn. Soc. (Zool.)* 28: 363-388.

DENNELL, R. (1937). On the feeding mechanism of *Apseudes talpa* and the evolution of the peracaridan feeding mechanisms. *Trans. roy. Soc. Edinb.* 59: 57-78.

FRYER, G. (1957). The feeding mechanism of some freshwater cyclopoid copepods. *Proc. zool. Soc. Lond.* 129: 1-25.

GARSTANG, W. (1896). Contributions to marine bionomics. I. The habits and respiratory mechanism of *Corystes cassivelaunus*. *J. mar. biol. Ass. U.K.* 4: 223-232.

GARSTANG, W. (1897). On some modifications of structure subservient to respiration in decapod Crustacea which burrow in sand; with some remarks on the utility of specific characters in the genus *Calappa*, and the description of a new species of *Albunea*. *Quart. J. micr. Sci.* 40: 211-232.

GREEN, J. (1957). The feeding mechanism of *Mesidotea entomon* (Linn.) (Crustacea: Isopoda). *Proc. zool. Soc. Lond.* 129: 245-254.

LOWNDES, A. G. (1935). The swimming and feeding of certain calanoid copepods. *Proc. zool. Soc. Lond.* ii, 687-715.

MANTON, S. M. (1928). On some points in the anatomy and habits of the lophogastrid Crustacea. *Trans. roy. Soc. Edinb.* 41: 103-119.

MANTON, S. M. (1930). Notes on the habits and feeding mechanisms of *Anaspides* and *Paranaspides*. *Proc. zool. Soc. Lond.* 791-800.

NICOL, E. A. T. (1932). The feeding habits of the Galatheida. *J. mar. biol. Ass. U.K.* 18: 87-106.

ROWETT, H. G. Q. (1943). The gut of Nebaliacea. *Discovery Rpts.* 23: 1-18.

CHAPTER III

BLOOD AND ITS CIRCULATION

SINCE the time when Harvey first watched the heart of a shrimp there has been a continual advance in our knowledge of the blood and its circulation in the Crustacea. The composition of the blood and the mechanism controlling its propulsion vary. The study of these variations has produced information on such diverse topics as the largest known molecules and the similarities of water fleas and men.

The concentration of salt in the blood, and its ionic composition, are important because animal tissues can only function properly when bathed in a liquid which maintains a fairly steady balance in its ionic composition. Excess of any one ion leads to changes in permeability, and to changes in the physical state of protoplasm, which, if severe enough, can completely disorganise it. The ionic composition of the blood is more important than the total concentration of salts, but the concentration of the fluid bathing cells cannot fall to a very low level without the danger of the cells swelling to the point of bursting.

Most Crustacea live in water, and if the concentration of the blood is higher than that of the water (as it is in freshwater Crustacea) then there will be a continuous tendency for water to flow into the body, and for salts to be lost from the body. Many freshwater Crustacea minimise these tendencies by having the outer covering almost completely impermeable, and restricting such surfaces as are necessary for exchange between blood and water to a limited area, such as the gills. Crustacea living in the sea do not have the same problem; the concentration of salt in their blood is similar to that of sea water, although some species (e.g. the prawn *Palaemon serratus*) keep their blood slightly less concentrated than sea water. The ionic composition of the blood often differs from that of sea water, indicating that the animals are actively regulating the proportions of the various ions, though it is not known exactly how they do this. One ion which varies from species to species is magnesium, and its concentration seems to vary inversely with the

39

activity of the species. For instance, in the sluggish stone crab (*Lithodes*) the concentration of magnesium is much higher than in the active prawns. Various other species can be arranged in a series between these two according to their activity and the concentration of magnesium in their blood.

Another important variable in the composition of the blood is the presence or absence of a respiratory pigment capable of combining loosely with oxygen and distributing it to the tissues. Two such pigments are found in Crustacea: haemocyanin and haemoglobin, but never together in one species.

The Decapoda and Stomatopoda have haemocyanin in the blood. This is a compound containing copper and a protein. It combines with oxygen in proportion to its copper content; two atoms of copper to one molecule of oxygen. When combined with oxygen it is blue, but when not so combined it is colourless. The molecular weight of haemocyanin is very high. If the weight combining with one molecule of oxygen is considered the molecular weight can be put at 74,000, but if the size of the particles in solution in the blood is considered then the figure is much higher; in the lobster it is about 640,000. In the prawn *Pandalus* and the crawfish *Palinurus* the particles in the blood have a molecular weight of 360,000. The crayfish, *Potamobius*, and the crabs *Cancer* and *Carcinus* have particles in the blood with both the molecular weights given above.

Although these molecular weights are large they do not compare with the haemocyanins of some molluscs, where a molecular weight of over six million has been recorded for the respiratory pigment of a snail. These large molecules are not just an accident, but appear to play a definite role in maintaining the osmotic concentration of the blood at a level similar to that of sea water. If the haemocyanin was dispersed in smaller more numerous particles the osmotic pressure of the blood would rise, and the animal would be confronted with a greater osmotic intake of water.

Haemoglobin has been found in the blood of the Anostraca, Notostraca, Conchostraca, Cladocera, some parasitic copepods, some harpacticid copepods, some ostracods, the branchiuran *Dolops*, and some of the parasitic Cirripedia.

The haemoglobin in Cladocera, particularly *Daphnia*, has been intensively studied by Prof. H. Munro Fox and his school. The blood of *Daphnia* is often bright red with haemoglobin, but the colour shows surprising fluctuations. These are due mainly to variations in the amount of oxygen in the water in which *Daphnia* lives. When there is little oxygen the blood is bright red; when oxygen is abundant the blood is pale. Individual animals can be changed from pale to red, and back to pale by appropriate alterations of the oxygen content of the water. The change from pale to red take about ten days, and the reverse change proceeds at the same rate. These changes are similar to those found in mountaineers when they become acclimatised to rarified air. The concentration of haemoglobin in their blood increases, and then decreases when they re-enter the denser air of the lowlands. The changes in *Daphnia* are the more spectacular, for the concentration of haemoglobin can increase twelvefold, whereas in man the concentration only increases by about one-fifth.

The function of haemoglobin in *Daphnia* has been demonstrated in a variety of ways. If red and pale specimens are put in stoppered bottles with water containing very little oxygen it is found that the red specimens survive much longer than the pale specimens. This indicates that the haemoglobin in the red specimens enables them to utilise oxygen which is not available to the pale specimens. This has been confirmed with another daphnid, *Simocephalus vetulus*; red specimens continue respiring at a greater rate than pale specimens when both are kept in low concentrations of oxygen.

The haemoglobin in red specimens can be rendered functionless by treating the animals with carbon monoxide. This gas combines with haemoglobin and prevents it from taking up oxygen. *Daphnia* which have been so treated are similar to pale specimens; they survive a shorter time in poorly aerated water than do red, untreated specimens. The treated individuals also move more slowly and collect less food than the untreated individuals, so that it is clear that the haemoglobin in red specimens enables them to gather more food than they could without the pigment.

Although oxygen is the dominant factor controlling the concentration of haemoglobin in *Daphnia*, other factors do play a part. In order to make haemoglobin *Daphnia* must be adequately fed, and there must be a certain amount of iron in the water, for iron is an essential part of the haemoglobin molecule. Temperature also plays a part. When the temperature increases the chemical processes of the body speed up—the metabolic rate is increased, and more oxygen is required to satisfy the animals' needs. If *Daphnia* is in poorly aerated water the increased demand for oxygen increases the relative deficiency of oxygen, so that the stimulus to synthesise haemoglobin is greater, and more haemoglobin is made. The effect of an increase in temperature is accentuated by the fact that haemoglobin has a lower affinity for oxygen at higher temperatures so that when the temperature is increased more haemoglobin is necessary to obtain the same amount of oxygen as was obtained at the lower temperature.

The effect of an increase in temperature, in increasing the metabolic rate, is paralleled by individual variations in activity. Males for instance are more active than females, they have a higher rate of oxygen consumption, and they have a higher concentration of haemoglobin in their blood than females kept in the same conditions. Similarly the small active *Daphnia curvirostris* has a higher concentration of haemoglobin than the larger, more sluggish *D. magna*, when both are in the same conditions. There are even races within one species of *Daphnia* which differ in their metabolic rates, and consequently differ in the concentration of haemoglobin in their blood. A British race of *Daphnia magna* has been found which makes more haemoglobin than a race of the same species from the south of France. The British race also grew faster and produced more eggs.

Haemoglobin is also found in the eggs of *Daphnia*, where it serves the function of enabling development to proceed in poorly aerated water. Eggs which have been treated with carbon monoxide develop more slowly than untreated eggs.

The functional basis of haemoglobin synthesis in relation to oxygen deficiency is easy to understand, but the reason why haemoglobin should be lost when *Daphnia* enters well aerated water is not at all clear. It is inevitable that the females should lose haemoglobin, because they pass it into their eggs, and if the water is well aerated they will not be stimulated to make more. When females are producing a large number of eggs this passage of haemoglobin into the eggs is sufficient to account for the usual rate of loss. However, males also lose haemoglobin and so do females which are producing few or no eggs. The second way in which haemoglobin is lost is by breakdown in the fat cells, which lie at the bases of the limbs and alongside the gut. Under certain conditions globules of haemoglobin can be seen in these cells. These globules eventually disappear and the blood is left pale. The distribution of iron in the tissues during haemoglobin breakdown also indicates the fat cells as the site of breakdown, and, further, indicates that the freed iron is excreted via the maxillary glands.

The story of haemoglobin in *Daphnia* is made more complicated by the presence of an allied pigment in the gut. This is a haemochromogen called daphniarubin. Haemochromogens of various sorts can be made from haemoglobin by suitable chemical treatment, and it is reasonable to assume that the pigment in the gut of *Daphnia* is derived from its haemoglobin. But there is no simple relationship between haemoglobin in the blood and haemochromogen in the gut, so that we cannot be certain that *Daphnia* makes such a conversion, except in one particular situation. We have already mentioned that *Daphnia* passes haemoglobin into its eggs; it has been noted that the concentration of haemoglobin decreases during embryonic development, and that once the gut of the embryo is formed haemochromogen begins to accumulate there in increasing amounts. In the embryos it would seem that haemoglobin is converted into haemochromogen.

A summary of the changes involved in the synthesis and breakdown of haemoglobin in *Daphnia* is given in fig. 25.

Only one other crustacean with haemoglobin in the blood has been studied in detail comparable with the studies on *Daphnia*. This is the brine shrimp, *Artemia salina*. In this species the concentration varies in much the same way as in *Daphnia*; there is more haemoglobin when oxygen is scarce. The amount of salt in the water where *Artemia* lives is often very high, and when this happens the oxygen content of the water is low, so that a false correlation appears between the salinity of the water and the haemo-

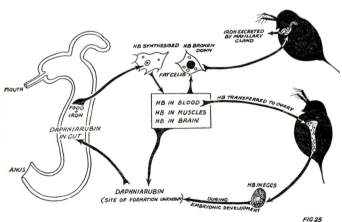

FIG. 25. Diagram showing the main routes of transference during the synthesis and breakdown of haemoglobin in *Daphnia*.

globin concentration in *Artemia*. The salinity is clearly an indirect factor, because it acts by decreasing the amount of oxygen that the water can hold.

Artemia differs from *Daphnia* in that the females make more haemoglobin per unit body size than the males. Another difference is that *Artemia* does not pass haemoglobin into its eggs. It does however produce resting eggs (p. 72) which have hard brown shells, and it has been found that these shells are very rich in a haem compound similar to the haemochromogen in the gut of *Daphnia*. It should be mentioned that *Artemia* also has a haemochromogen in the gut and thus differs from the notostracan, *Triops cancriformis*, which also produces eggs with shells rich in haemochromogen, but does not have such a pigment in its gut.

The blood pigments of the Crustacea are not contained in cells, they are dissolved in the plasma. The only cells in the blood are those which correspond with the white cells in mammals. In many Crustacea there appears to be only one type of blood cell. *Artemia*, for instance, has blood cells which vary in diameter from $10\text{-}15\mu$; they are normally more or less spherical, but they often adhere to various organs and creep about in an amoeboid manner. *Daphnia* has similar, but smaller blood cells $7\text{-}8\mu$ in diameter. Crabs and lobsters have several types of blood cells which might be progressive stages in the development of a single type. The blood cells are formed in special organs which occur at the bases of the limbs (in *Artemia*), on the wall of the stomach (in the crayfish), in the head (in Amphipoda) or on the surface of the ventral artery (in Stomatopoda). Each organ is formed from a group of cells surrounded by a thin membrane. The cells within the membrane all look alike, but show various stages in division. The newly formed blood cells presumably escape through the thin membrane into the blood.

The blood cells perform various functions. They are active in resisting infection by bacteria and fungi. Metchnikoff (1884) first gave a detailed account of this process and realised its importance in resistance to diseases; he found a population of *Daphnia magna* which was infected with a yeast-like fungus which produces long, needle-like spores. These spores penetrate the gut of *Daphnia* and enter the blood, where they germinate and reproduce. Eventually the whole body-cavity may be filled with spores, but a high percentage of the individuals which become infected manage to combat the infection. The blood cells gather around the spores and destroy them.

Another function of the blood cells is to plug small wounds. The cells gather around the wound and form a mass in which all the cell bodies unite. This mass serves as a stopgap until the tissues around the wound can regenerate and repair the damage.

Some of the blood cells are concerned with the transport of materials around the body. This is particularly well shown in the shore crab when it is about to moult. Large blood cells are found, filled with a lipoprotein substance, which is similar to that forming the outer layer of the cuticle. When the crab moults these cells disappear. These lipoprotein cells appear to transport the material to the bases of the epidermal cells so that they can use it to manufacture the outer layer of the exoskeleton. It is not certain where the blood cells get the lipoprotein from, or whether they make it themselves.

The mechanism for circulating the blood of Crustacea is variable. Some crustaceans (e.g. harpacticid copepods) do not have a heart. This seems to be connected with their small size; the blood moves sufficiently when the animal moves its limbs.

When a heart is present it lies in the dorsal part of the body, just beneath the exoskeleton. Fig. 26 gives some idea of the range of shape and position of the heart and main arteries. The cavity containing the heart is separated from the rest of the body cavity by a membrane, the pericardium. Blood enters the heart from the pericardial cavity. Small valves, or ostia, allow the entry, but not the exit of blood. When the heart contracts the blood is forced out through other apertures, which may, or may not be continued into an arterial system. In *Daphnia* there is a single exit at the front of the heart, which is slightly drawn out to form a very short 'aorta'. In contrast, the Decapoda and Isopoda have an elaborate system of arteries leaving the heart in various directions. The venous system is represented by ill defined sinuses. Generally, there is a large sternal sinus, below the gut; this sinus communicates with the cavities of the gills and the limbs. A series of canals runs from the gills upwards to the pericardial cavity. In some species, such as the crayfish, these canals are narrow and well defined enough to be called branchio-cardiac veins.

When the heart contracts its volume naturally diminishes, and pressure within the pericardium is lowered; this results in blood being drawn into the pericardial cavity. The filling of the crustacean heart is a very different process from that in mammals, where the blood circulates in closed vessels throughout its course and so must eventually be pushed back into the heart. In order for the crustacean heart to suck in blood it must have a mechanism for actively expanding after it has contracted. This is provided in two ways. The elasticity of the heart tends to return it to its normal shape, and, of more importance, the heart is connected to the hard outer covering of the body by elastic fibres. When the heart con-

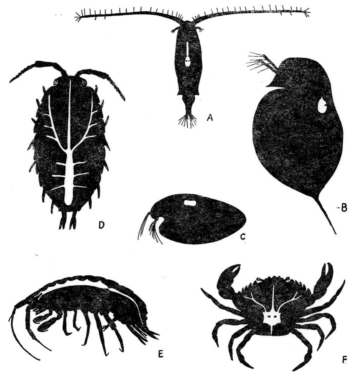

Fig. 26. Diagrams showing the heart and main arteries in certain Crustacea. A, a calanoid copepod. B, *Daphnia*. C, a myodocopan ostracod. D, an isopod, *Ligia*. E, an amphipod, *Gammarus*. F, a crab, *Carcinus*. The outlines are not all drawn to the same scale.

tracts these fibres are stretched, and their elasticity pulls the heart back to its shape before contraction, filling it with blood from the pericardial cavity. Valves at the beginnings of the arteries prevent blood from flowing back into the heart from the arteries.

The circulatory system of a crustacean is obviously not one in which any great pressure can be developed. The fact that the arteries open into comparatively large spaces prevents the development of high pressures. In the lobster the pressure in the main artery when the heart contracts is only 7·35 mm. of mercury; in man the corresponding figure would be 120.

The rate of beating of the crustacean heart is remarkably variable (Table 2), not only in different kinds of Crustacea, but within one species. Sometimes, as in *Daphnia*, the heart can stop for short periods with no great harm. Many external factors influence the rate of beat, producing effects that are quite different from anything in the mammalian heart. The hearts of some of the transparent Crustacea beat quicker in response to an increase in light intensity, and slow down when the light is reduced. An increase in temperature has a similar effect to an increase in light intensity. The rate of beat may be doubled by a rise of 10° C. These effects of light and heat show that the crustacean heart is much more at the mercy of the elements than the heart of a mammal, which is concealed beneath an opaque outer covering, and is housed in a body which maintains a fairly constant temperature.

TABLE 2

Rate of heart beat in various Crustacea. The figures are very approximate, and are subject to variation with the size of the individuals.

(Data extracted from Schwartzkopff, 1955)

Species	Temperature °C.	Beats per minute
Daphnia pulex	5	75
	10	150
	20	500
Asellus aquaticus	5	50
	10	110
	20	250
Gammarus pulex	5	100
	10	125
	20	250
Palinurus vulgaris	10	50
	20	100
Leander serratus	5	60
	10	80
	20	150

As well as being influenced by external factors the crustacean heart is also controlled by an internal mechanism. The analysis of this mechanism has provided some surprises. A comparison with the mammalian heart will illustrate these. The rhythm of a mammalian heart originates in a patch of muscular tissue in the heart, and spreads over the rest of the heart from this pacemaker. The heart continues beating with a steady rhythm when all the nerves leading to it are cut. A heart of this type, where the rhythm originates in the muscular tissue of the heart, is termed myogenic. The nerves which supply the heart merely provide a fine adjusting mechanism. One set of nerves (sympathetic) accelerates the heart, while the other (parasympathetic) slows it down. Most Crustacea have a heart of a different type, in which the beat originates in nerve cells on the wall of the heart. This type of heart is termed neurogenic. The two types of heart differ in their reactions to certain drugs. The mammalian heart is accelerated by adrenaline, which is produced at the ends of the sympathetic nerves, while it is slowed by acetylcholine, which is produced by the parasympathetic fibres. The hearts of most Crustacea are accelerated by acetylcholine. Surprisingly they are also accelerated by adrenaline, so that here the two substances are not antagonistic. Exceptions to the general rule among the Crustacea are found in the Cladocera. Acetycholine slows the heart of *Daphnia*, so that it appears to be myogenic, but the situation is not identical with that in the mammals, for no clear effect of adrenaline has been found.

LITERATURE

Fox, H. M. (1948). The haemoglobin of *Daphnia*. Proc. Roy Soc. B. 135: 195-212.

Fox, H. M. (1955). The effect of oxygen on the concentration of haem in invertebrates. Proc. Roy. Soc. B. 143: 203-214.

Fox, H. M. (1957). Haemoglobin in Crustacea. New Biology 24: 60-77.

Gilchrist, B. M. (1954). Haemoglobin in *Artemia*. Proc. Roy. Soc. B. 143: 136-146.

Green, J. (1955). Haemoglobin in the fat-cells of *Daphnia*. Quart J. Micr. Sci. 96: 173-176.

GREEN, J. (1956). Variation in the haemoglobin content of *Daphnia.* *Proc. Roy. Soc.* B. 145: 214-232.

KRIJGSMAN, B. J. (1952). Contractile and pacemaker mechanisms of the heart of arthopods. *Biol. Rev.* 27: 320-346.

METCHNIKOFF, E. (1884). Ueber eine Sprosspilzkrankheit der Daphniden. Beitrag zur Lehre über den Kampf der Phagocyten gegen Krankheitserreger. *Virchows Arch.* 9: 177-195.

PHEAR, E. A. (1955). Gut haems in invertebrates. *Proc. zool. Soc. Lond.* 125: 383-406.

REDFIELD, A. C. (1934). The Haemocyanins. *Biol. Rev.* 9: 175-212.

ROBERTSON, J. D. (1957). Osmotic and ionic regulation in aquatic invertebrates. In: *Recent advances in invertebrate physiology.* Oregon.

SCHWARTZKOPFF, J. (1955). Vergleichende Untersuchungen der Herzfrequenz bei Krebsen. *Biol. Zentralb.* 74: 480-497.

SEWELL, M. T. (1955). Lipo-protein cells in the blood of *Carcinus maenas,* and their cycle of activity correlated with the moult. *Quart. J. micr. Sci.* 96: 73-83.

CHAPTER IV

COLOURS

THE variation in colour and pattern among Crustacea is so great that a mere catalogue would be larger than this book. Some of the colours can be related to a particular crustacean's way of life, but other colours appear to be functionless, though this may only be due to our ignorance.

Many crustaceans have concealing coloration, and merge successfully with their backgrounds. The common Porcelain Crab, *Porcellana platycheles*, of European shores, is often extremely difficult to spot when a stone is turned over because its colour and texture match the mixed growth of plants and animals coating the underside of the stone. Sometimes the colours are specially adapted to a particularly limited environment. The small crab *Huenia proteus* has a body shaped like a part of the calcareous green seaweed *Halimeda*, and its colour matches that of the alga so closely that detection is extremely difficult.

Crustaceans belonging to different groups sometimes show parallel adaptive coloration. An alpheid shrimp, a squat lobster, a porcelain crab and a spider crab are all found among colonies of *Spongodes*, which is a relative of the sea anemones, found in Indian Seas. The four different Crustacea are all coloured greyish-white with pink spots so that they resemble parts of the colony on which they live. Shrimps with alternate bands of yellow and purple sound most conspicuous, but several species are known which live on a sea lily (not a plant, but an animal belonging to the Echinodermata) coloured in the same way.

Sometimes an animal is more conspicuous because of the shadow that it casts. The ghost crab *Ocypode ceratophthalma* is coloured like the tropical sands over which it runs at great speed. When running it holds its body high on long legs, and the shadow that it casts is more conspicuous than its body. When alarmed this crab races away wildly, then suddenly stops and lowers its body close against the sand so that its shadow disappears. The body is very flat so that when pressed against the sand it does not cast a shadow. In this way the crab can apparently disappear.

As a contrast to concealing coloration some Crustacea have strikingly conspicuous patterns which act as warnings to their predators. The best example is the African Land Crab, *Sesarma meinerti*, which has a purple back bordered with orange, and bright red chelae which it waves threateningly in the air. If caught away from cover this crab does not flee in the way that the Ghost Crab would, but stands its ground and will fight with considerable pugnacity. The contrasting pattern and conspicuous chelae advertise its powers of retaliation if attacked, and in fact it is rarely attacked. There are records of an allied species successfully defending itself from the attacks of small dogs.

The pattern of coloration often varies within a species, the Shore Crab *Carcinus maenas* is particularly variable when young; patches of green, yellow, white or red form a variety of patterns on the backs of crabs about an inch across, but when the crabs reach larger sizes they become more uniform in colour, with dark backs and paler undersides.

One of the most striking examples of variation in pattern and colour within a species is found in the small shrimp *Hippolyte varians*. A number of variants, all captured on the same day at Brighton are illustrated in fig. 27. The young specimens in particular show great variation in pattern, and as a rule the pattern is effective in concealing the shrimp on a particular seaweed. If

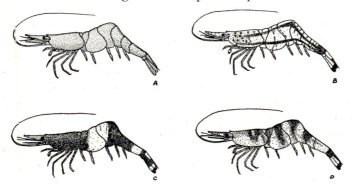

FIG. 27. *Hippolyte varians* (Decapoda Natantia, Caridea), showing variation in colour and pattern. All the patterns have been imposed on a standard outline. A, uniform pale green; uniformly brown specimens were also found. B, transparent, with pattern dominated by two longitudinal red lines. C and D disruptive brown patterns.

given the choice of several seaweeds a young *Hippolyte* will choose the one which its own pattern matches best. This shrimp can also change colour to a remarkable extent, particularly at night, when, no matter what the daytime pattern may be, the whole body becomes a beautiful translucent blue. When daylight returns the characteristic daytime pattern of the individual is again apparent.

Most crustacean colours are due to pigments. These are chemical substances which absorb certain of the colours present in white light and reflect others. The colour of a pigment is that of the light it reflects or transmits. There are other ways of producing colour, which depend upon light being split into its component colours by various physical systems, such as thin films of certain substances, or layers of transparent materials which bend the rays of light to varying degrees. These structural colours can often be recognised by the fact that they change according to the direction of the light falling on the surface bearing the colour. In general, structural colours are not very important in Crustacea, but they can be seen, for instance, in the iridescent eyes of some species and on the shiny hairs or bristles on some crustacean limbs.

Some crustacean colours are, in a sense, accidental. The gut of transparent species is often visible and is coloured by its contents, particularly in plant-eating species, where it may be bright green due to the accumulation of chlorophyll and its breakdown products. The red colour of haemoglobin in the blood can be regarded in the same way. The pigment is important in the physiology of *Daphnia* and certain other Crustacea (p. 40), but the resulting red colour has no function in concealment or advertisement; it is merely incidental to the respiratory physiology of its possessor.

Other pigments which appear to be accidents are the bile pigments found in the roots of some parasitic cirripedes, such as *Peltogaster* (see p. 116), and in the liver of an American crayfish *Cambarus*. Bile pigments are formed from the breakdown of haemoglobin in mammals and other vertebrates, but some of the Crustacea in which bile pigments are found have no haemoglobin, so that they may be formed in some other way, probably by the breakdown of other haem compounds, such as cytochrome, which plays a part in the respiratory processes within cells. Some ostracods accumulate bile pigments in the wall of their gut. The pigment is only found when the animals have been feeding on blue green algae, which have bile pigments as part of their light-absorbing system. When an ostracod with bile pigment in its gut wall is transferred to a diet of green algae (which have no bile pigments) the pigment slowly disappears.

The most obvious and important pigments in the Crustacea are the carotenoids. These, as their names implies, are chemically related to the colour in carrots; in fact one of the most abundant of the carotenoids in Crustacea is β-carotene, which is the main pigment in carrots. Astaxanthin is another abundant carotenoid; it is responsible for the red colour of many different crustaceans. It is also responsible for the blue colour of the lobster; the blue is formed when the astaxanthin is linked with a particular protein. The familiar change in the colour of the lobster when boiled is due to the denaturation of the protein and the breaking of its link with the carotenoid pigment. A similar pigment, but more violet in colour is found in the eggs of the hermit crab *Eupagurus bern-hardus*. The eggs often contain so much of this pigment that they appear to be black in colour. Lobster eggs are green in colour; this is also due to astaxanthin linked to a protein, and shows the same change to red when the eggs are boiled. The change to red is also shown naturally by the embryos towards the end of development; the green colour disappears, and the embryos become red. A similar change is found in the eggs of *Daphnia magna*. The green colour is found dispersed through the whole of the cytoplasm of the new laid egg, but at the end of development the red colour is found to be in small fat globules. This change in the location of the pigment is due to a change in solubility when the protein link is broken. When linked with protein the pigment is soluble in water, but when the protein link is broken the freed pigment is only soluble in fats and similar substances.

The amount of carotenoid in the body and eggs of *Daphnia magna* has recently been found to be influenced by light. Specimens kept in continuous light deposited three times as much carotenoid in the fat body and eggs as specimens kept in the dark, even though both groups were fed identically. The process can be reversed by transferring specimens from the light to darkness, when after several days they lose some of their colour.

These experiments are relevant to the coloration of cave crustacea, most of which are white or transparent. This lack of colour seems to be due to the lack of light in caves, and some cave species have been found to gain colour when exposed to light for a number of weeks.

It might be expected that Crustacea from the deep sea might

also be colourless, but this is not so. Many deep sea Crustacea, particularly the bathypelagic decapods (see p. 131) are a uniform brilliant red in colour; at least that is how they are coloured when brought to the surface. There is the possibility that when they are in the depths they are not so coloured, but maintain the translucent blue that *Hippolyte varians* assumes at night. Nevertheless, it can be argued that red is the best concealing colour for Crustacea in the middle depths, where red light has all been absorbed. In the dim light of moderate depths a red crustacean would appear black and so be quite inconspicuous. But inconspicuousness does not appear to be the aim of many of these Crustacea; they compensate for their apparent blackness by having luminescent organs.

Luminescent organs may be divided into two types: those which discharge a luminescent fluid into the water, and those which produce a light in a distinct position on the body of the animal. The two types probably serve different functions. Those which discharge a luminous fluid usually do so when the crustacean is agitated, so that they may serve to produce a luminescent patch which would act as a diversion when the crustacean is attacked. The non-discharging lights may well act as signals to other members of the same species, and serve as part of a mechanism for producing swarms in which the chances of meeting a sexual partner in the breeding season are increased. It has been calculated that the luminescent organs of a *Euphausia* may be visible to another *Euphausia* at a distance of a hundred feet, so that if the lights really are a stimulus to swarming they could operate over a wide area.

Most of the luminescence produced by Crustacea is produced by chemicals made in the bodies of the crustaceans themselves. But there are some luminous bacteria which infect Crustacea and give the whole animal a glow. In Lake Suwa, Japan, there is a fresh-water shrimp, *Xiphocaridina compressa* which is frequently infected with the bacterium *Microspira phosphoreum*. On hot summer nights the shrimps swarm at the surface of the lake, and the luminescence provided by the bacteria is of such beauty that the shrimp is protected by a government order. Bacteria are also responsible for the known cases of luminosity among isopods and amphipods.

The luminescence discharged into the water by Crustacea has proved to be most suitable for the study of the mechanism of light production. The ostracod *Cypridina hilgendorfi* in particular has been subjected to much study, and has been shown to possess one of the simplest systems of light production. Two substances are produced in a gland which discharges them into the water. When the two substances, called luciferin and luciferase, are mixed in the presence of oxygen the luciferin becomes oxidised and this process excites the luciferase to produce light. The interesting feature of this reaction is that the oxidation of luciferin is catalysed by luciferase, so that the latter plays the dual role of an activator, and of a substance which becomes activated. Luciferin and luciferase are present in the discharges of other luminescent crustaceans, but they show a certain degree of specificity. The luciferase of a decapod will not produce light with luciferin from *Cypridina*, but the luciferase from *Cypridina* will produce light with luciferin from another ostracod, *Pyrocypris*.

The chemistry of the non-discharging light organs in the bodies of Crustacea has not yet been worked out, but it may well prove to be more complicated than the system found in *Cypridina*. Other animals with non-discharging luminescent organs, such as fireflies, need other substances as well as luciferin, luciferase and oxygen before they can produce light.

The dark colours of Crustacea are due to two different types of pigment which have been confused in the past; these are the melanins and the ommochromes. The latter pigments are found particularly in the eyes of Crustacea, but they also colour the body; for instance, the brown colour of the shrimp *Crangon* is due to ommochromes, so is the dark pigmentary pattern of the water slater *Asellus*. A curious feature concerning the distribution of melanin in the decapods is that it is only found in the Brachyura, and when found it is associated with considerable concentrations of riboflavin, which is an important component of the vitamin B complex, but we do not know why this association occurs.

The eyes of many Crustacea contain white reflecting pigments, whose chemical nature is uncertain, but pterins have been identified in the eyes of a number of decapods. The pterins were at one time thought to be end products of the metabolism of nitrogen-containing substances in the body, but they now appear to play an active part in the chemistry of an animal; the various functions which have been discovered, or suggested, include a part in the manufacture of melanin and in the chemistry of vision. The pterins are usually coloured yellow, and one such pigment, xanthopterin, or at least something very similar to it, has been isolated from the carapace of the edible crab *Cancer pagurus*. Several pterins are colourless, but in ultra-violet light they fluoresce brilliantly.

There are other pigments in Crustacea, but we know very little about them; one such pigment is the green colour found in some ostracods and in the Notostraca. This turns brown when alkalis are added to it, but returns to green in acid, and it is decolorised by reducing agents, regaining its colour in aerated water.

When a crustacean colour is functional, for instance in conceal-ment, the pigment is usually near the outer covering, most often in special structures called chromatophores. These are sometimes very elaborate, formed from several cells and having numerous branches which radiate from a central body. The most complex types contain four different pigments. *Crangon* has some chromato-

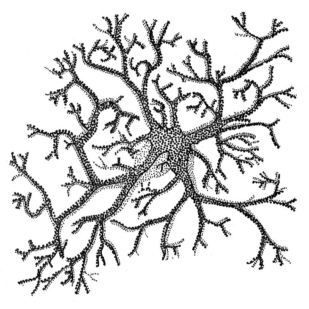

Fig. 28. Diagram of a dichromatic chromatophore in the fully expanded state. The structure is shown as being in two dimensions, but the branches frequently extend in all directions. The branches of the paler pigment follow those of the darker pigment very closely.

phores with black, white, yellow and red branches, while *Penaeus* has some with white, yellow, red and blue branches. It is only in the Decapoda Natantia that such multicoloured chromatophores are found, most other groups can only muster one or two colours in a single chromatophore. When a single colour is found in a chromatophore a separate name may be given to indicate the colour: melanophores are black, erythrophores are red and xanthophores are yellow.

The chromatophores are the effectors by means of which a crustacean can change colour. If the pigment extends into all the branches the whole surface of the animal becomes darker. When the pigment contracts into the small central area the colour becomes much lighter, and, in the less heavily calcified species, more transparent.

These changes can be seen at their simplest in an isopod such as *Ligia*, which, if placed in the light on a dark background, expands its chromatophores and becomes dark in colour. When placed on a white background the chromatophores contract and the body becomes paler. The complete change takes about two hours. These changes are clearly an aid to concealment.

If the lighting arrangements of *Ligia's* world are turned upside down some interesting results are obtained. When lit from below, with a black background above it, *Ligia* is paler than when lit from above with a black background beneath it. This suggests that *Ligia* is sensitive to the light coming up from the surface on which it stands, and can adjust its colour accordingly. The obvious organs to examine for such sensitivity are the eyes. By covering different parts of the eyes with an opaque paint it has been found that it is the light reflected from the background and perceived by the lower parts of the eyes which initiates colour change. If the lower parts of the eyes are painted over the isopod becomes dark in colour irrespective of its background.

It has been suggested that the colour change in *Ligia* is under the control of two hormones. One causes contraction of the melanophores and is produced when the lower parts of the eyes are illuminated. The other causes expansion of the melanophores and is produced when the upper parts of the eyes are illuminated. The colour assumed by the isopod will depend on the balance between the two hormones. If this is really so, then maximum paling should occur when the lower parts of the eyes are illuminated, but not the upper parts. In fact it is found that when the upper parts of the eyes are painted over the animals become paler than if the eyes are left unpainted.

The site of production of the colour-change hormones in *Ligia* is not accurately known, but it seems certain that a hormone which causes the black chromatophores to contract is produced in the head. A great deal more is known about hormones in the decapods.

The method of establishing that an organ is the site of hormone production is to remove the organ, observe the resulting condition of the animal, and then restore its normal functions by injections of extract from the same organs or by implanting such organs in the body. Confirmatory methods include staining the organ in such a way that will show if it is secretory, and by observations on the rate of change of a process as the organ regenerates after removal, but these cannot replace the method of ablation followed by restoration of function.

Using methods similar to those described above it has been shown that the nervous system of the Crustacea contains the most important sites of hormone production.

In general plan the nervous system consists of a brain, lying above the oesophagus, connected to a chain of ganglia which lie beneath the gut. The first ganglion in the chain is the sub-oesophageal ganglion (fig. 29). The brain and the sub-oesophageal ganglion give off nerves to the antennae and the mouthparts. The two nerves connecting the brain with the sub-oesophageal ganglion are known as the circum-oesophageal commissures. In fig. 29 the main sites of hormone secretion are indicated by the dark cells which have fibres leading out to storage and releasing sites.

The eyestalks house a complex arrangement for the production

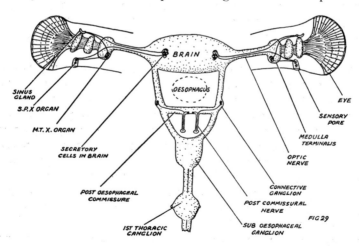

FIG. 29. Diagram of the front part of the nervous system of a decapod, to show the location of some important centres of hormone secretion.

and release of hormones. The sinus gland receives its name because it lies alongside a small blood sinus. It is doubtful whether it actually secretes hormones itself, but there is no doubt that large quantities of hormones are found in it. These hormones pass along fibres leading from cells located in the brain and in the X-organ in the medulla terminalis (M.T. X organ). In some species there are additional fibres leading to the sinus gland which seem to come from other parts of the nervous system. The sinus gland is probably best regarded as a reservoir and releasing point of hormones.

A similar release point is found in the region just behind the post-oesophageal commissure. Two fine nerves, the post-commissure nerves, leave the commissure and end in flat plates which are partly joined to the wall of a blood sinus. This region of the nervous system is particularly rich in hormones which control colour change. The details of these substances are complicated and not yet fully worked out; a review and introduction to the vast literature is given by Knowles and Carlisle (1956). The situation is complicated further by the fact that crabs and prawns differ in details of chromatophore control. Substances have been extracted from the eyestalks and post-oesophageal commissures of prawns which cause the chromatophores to contract their pigments, and a melanophore expanding substance has been extracted from the sub-oesophageal ganglion of the crab *Uca*. In this latter creature there is evidence that six hormones may be involved in its colour control; expanding and contracting substances are produced for the red, white and black chromatophores. However, it must not be thought that the hormones are always specific for chromatophores of a particular colour. In *Leander* one substance is capable of causing contraction of the red pigment in the white-red-yellow chromatophores, and simultaneously causing expansion of red pigment in the red-yellow chromatophores.

Further studies on *Uca* have shown that it has a rhythm of colour change that is remarkably persistent. The crab is pale at night and dark during the day, and it will maintain the change from pale to dark and back again in a regular rhythm even when kept in constant darkness at a constant temperature for as long as two months. A curious additional feature is that the time of maximum darkening shows a rhythm which is tuned to the tides. The time of greatest expansion of the melanophores becomes about fifty minutes later with each successive day, and the time coincides with a period of about an hour before low tide. The daytime darkening and the coincidence of maximum darkening with the period just before low tide are aids to concealment when the crab is active. Foraging and locomotory activity of *Uca* are at their peak just before low tide.

The time of low tide varies from locality to locality, and crabs collected from beaches which differ in the times of low tide maintain their own particular rhythm of melanophore expansion when kept in darkness in the laboratory, so that their cycle corresponds with that of their fellows remaining on the beaches.

It is evident that these crabs have an internal clock of considerable accuracy. We do not know how they measure their time, but it does not seem to be due to ordinary metabolic processes, because the mechanism is, to a large extent, independent of temperature. The crabs maintain a steady rhythm at all temperatures between 6 and 26° C. However, if a crab is cooled to 2 or 3° C. its clock is slowed by about the duration of the chilling. In this way it is possible to reset the clock, but once the crab is returned to normal temperatures its natural rhythm of colour change reappears with its accuracy unimpaired apart from being behind that of its untreated fellows.

One final factor involved in the precise degree of expansion of the chromatophores of *Uca* is the incidence of cosmic radiation. This factor is rarely taken into consideration in biological experiments, but if *Uca* is shielded from cosmic rays by sheets of lead its melanophores expand more than they do if the crab is not so shielded. The atmosphere also acts as a shield against cosmic rays. When barometric pressure is high fewer rays penetrate to the surface of the earth. An apparent correlation between melanophore expansion and changes in barometric pressure can be found, but the effect is due to cosmic radiation, not to the direct effect of air pressure. This has been shown by experiments in which crabs were kept in chambers at constant pressure; the rhythm of the crabs was not affected by the local constancy of pressure.

Is it possible that the crabs use a diurnal cycle of cosmic radiation to adjust their own clocks? A recent experiment, made in America, was designed to test whether the crabs could maintain their rhythm when there was no possible external factor which could give them a clue. A group of crabs was collected from the Atlantic coast, and half were sealed in an opaque tub and flown to the Pacific coast. In making this trip the normal diurnal cycle of factors due to rotation of the earth was extended to over 27 hours. In spite of this the crabs, kept in darkness for the next six days, maintained their normal rhythm and remained synchronised with their fellows kept in darkness on the Atlantic coast. The conclusion is that *Uca* has an internal clock which can function without external clues.

LITERATURE

BROWN, F. A. (1957). The rhythmic nature of life. In: *Recent advances in invertebrate physiology*, pp. 287-304.

BUSNEL, R. G., & DRILHON, A. (1948). Sur les pigments flaviniques et pteriniques des Crustaces. *Bull. Soc. zool. Fr.* 73: 143-185.

COTT, H. B. (1929). Observations on the natural history of the land-crab *Sesarma meinerti*, from Beira, with special reference to the theory of warning colours. *Proc. zool. Soc. Lond.* 1929 ii: 679-692.

DENNELL, R. (1955). Observations on the luminescence of bathy-pelagic Crustacea Decapoda of the Bermuda area. *J. Linn. Soc. (Zool.)* 42: 393-406.

GREEN, J. (1957). Carotenoids in *Daphnia*. *Proc. Roy. Soc.* B. 147: 392-401.

JOHNSON, F. H., Ed. (1955). *The luminescence of biological systems*. Washington.

KNOWLES, F. G. W., & CARLISLE, D. B. (1956). Endocrine control in the Crustacea. *Biol. Rev.* 31: 396-473.

NICOL, J. A. C. (1958). Observations on luminescence in pelagic animals. *J. mar. biol. Ass. U.K.* 37: 705-752.

SMITH, H. G. (1938). The receptive mechanism of the background response in chromatic behaviour of Crustacea. *Proc. Roy. Soc.* B. 125: 250.

CHAPTER V

GROWTH AND LIFE HISTORIES

A L L the typical Crustacea grow in a series of steps. The presence of a hard outer covering prevents any increase in size, except immediately after moulting, when the new skeleton is still soft and extensible. The life of most Crustacea is thus divided into intervals between moults. These intervals may be further subdivided according to the condition of the skeleton at the various stages. Carlisle and Dohrn have produced a classification based upon their studies of decapods, but essentially the same stages can be recognised in other Crustacea, although the references to calcification do not always apply.

> *Stage 1. Proecdysis or premoult*—calcium is removed from the exoskeleton, and the calcium content of the blood increases. A new skeleton is laid down beneath the old one. New setae can be seen forming.
>
> *Stage 2. Ecdysis or moult*—the actual shedding of the old exoskeleton; the animal swells by taking up water.
>
> *Stage 3. Metecdysis or postmoult*—the exoskeleton is being hardened and calcified. Crabs and crayfish do not feed during this stage, and do not expose themselves unnecessarily.
>
> *Stage 4. Intermoult*—the animal is in normal condition, with a hard exoskeleton. This stage varies in duration. When there is a long interval between a metecdysis and the next proecdysis the term anecdysis is applied to the intermoult, but when the metecdysis passes almost immediately into a proecdysis the term diecdysis is applied. Some Crustacea, after passing through several moults, reach a stage where they do not moult again; this can be called a terminal anecdysis.

The mechanical process of moulting is often hazardous. It has long been recognised by people who have kept Crustacea in aquaria that difficulties during moulting, and failure to complete a moult give rise to a large proportion of the deaths which occur.

The old skeleton is split along definite pre-formed lines. In the lobster, for instance, the skeleton splits between the carapace and the abdomen, and the body is withdrawn through the hole leaving the old skeleton practically intact. In the isopods the skeleton is cast in two parts, and the front portion may be cast several days after the hind portion. Some Cladocera, such as *Ilyocryptus* and *Monospilus*, do not completely cast the carapace at each moult, so that they accumulate a series of carapaces on their back. One other cladoceran, *Alonopsis elongata*, has a similar habit which appears to be of survival value. *Chaetogaster diaphanus* is a worm which feeds on small Crustacea; in a survey of its feeding habits in Windermere it was found that *Alonopsis elongata* occurred many fewer times in the worm's gut than one would expect from its abundance in the immediate vicinity of the worm. This could be explained by the fact that *A. elongata* carries one or two old carapaces, out of which it can escape if trapped.

Long, delicate setae, such as those on the antennae of *Daphnia*, present certain problems during ecdysis. These problems are overcome by the setae developing in pockets formed by their own bases. During moulting these pockets are extroverted and the setae extended (fig. 30). The extension of these setae illustrates the delicate balance between success and failure in moulting. Extension depends

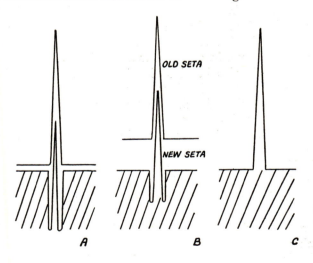

Fig. 30. Diagram to show the formation of new setae during moulting. The new seta lies partly within the old seta and partly tucked back in the newly formed cuticle.

on the fractional pull on the tip of the seta as it is withdrawn from the old seta. If there is not sufficient friction the seta is not extended, if there is too much the animal is stuck and encumbered with at least a part of its old skeleton.

The process of moulting is controlled by hormones, which are secreted by various glands. Some of these glands have already been described in the chapter on colours (p. 58). If the eyestalks of a crayfish are removed the animal moults earlier than it would otherwise. Now, if sinus glands are implanted in the operated crayfish the moult is delayed. This is a clear indication that a moult-inhibiting hormone is present in the sinus gland. There is also evidence, from other experiments, that a moult-inhibiting hormone may sometimes be produced by the brain.

A moult-accelerating hormone has also been found, surprisingly also in the eyestalks, but not in the sinus gland. In *Lysmata* this hormone appears to be produced in the medulla terminalis X organ (see fig. 29, p. 58).

An interesting situation has been found in relation to the dual control of moulting in the prawn *Leander serratus*. It was found that removal of the eyestalks of specimens from Roscoff led to an increase in the rate of moulting, whereas if the eyestalks were removed from Plymouth specimens a decreased rate of moulting was the result. It is clear that the hormone balance in the two populations is different, though the nature of the difference is not known. It may be due to a different rate of production of moult-controlling hormones in other parts of the body.

The Y-organ is also involved in the control of moulting. This organ, which lies in the head, seems to produce a hormone which is the actual stimulant for the onset of proecdysis, and the suggestion has been made that the moult-accelerating and inhibiting hormones act via their effects on the Y-organ. The role of the Y-organ in relation to the terminal anecdysis of crabs has recently been elucidated by Carlisle. There are two possibilities in explaining the lack of any further moulting. One is that the Y-organ degenerates and no longer produces the moult-promoting hormone; the other is that the Y-organ does not degenerate, but is inhibited by excessive production of moult-inhibiting hormone. Both these mechanisms have been shown to operate in different species of crabs. *Maia squinado* does not moult once it has become sexually mature, and at the same time its Y-organ degenerates. *Carcinus maenas* continues moulting while sexually mature, but eventually enters terminal anecdysis after about ten moults from the onset of maturity. The Y-organ of *Carcinus* does not degenerate, but when it enters its terminal anecdysis the crab is prevented from moulting by an excessive secretion of moult-inhibiting hormone by the X organ-sinus gland complex. If the eyestalks of *Carcinus* in terminal anecdysis are removed then the crab may moult, and larger specimens than usual may be produced by this means.

The hormonal system controlling moulting does not act independently of the environment. Moulting may be inhibited by unfavourable conditions of various kinds. Prolonged starvation is an obvious example, but moulting of the crab *Gecarcinus lateralis* is also inhibited by continuous light, by high temperatures, and even by the absence of a suitable burrow. This last factor indicates that the hormonal system may be influenced by physical contact of the animal with its sheltering place. This is of some importance to a crab because it is more vulnerable than usual after moulting, and having a shelter will increase its chance of survival.

The swelling which occurs when the old skeleton is cast is due to the intake of water. This process is also under hormonal control. When the eyestalks of the crab *Carcinus* are removed a day or so before moulting the operated crabs swell to a greater size than unoperated controls.

The hormone which controls water intake appears to be different from that which inhibits moulting. The Plymouth population of *Carcinus maenas* only produces the moult-inhibiting hormone in its eyestalks during the three coldest months of the year; at other times brain secretions are responsible for moult inhibition. However, removal of the eyestalks at any time of year results in an increased swelling at a moult.

Swelling after a moult is a comparatively rapid process; in the crayfish the increase in size is completed in about six hours. In smaller Crustacea the process is much more rapid; *Daphnia* completes its swelling within a minute. Such a rapid intake of water must result in a dilution of the blood, and this has been found to be so in a wide range of Crustacea. The concentration of the blood is usually restored to normal within a short space of time. This temporary dilution of the blood produces an odd effect in *Daphnia*, where a disturbance of the heart rate for about five minutes after moulting has been observed. This may be explained by the dilution of certain ions, some of which, such as potassium, have important effects on the rate and strength of the heart beat.

F

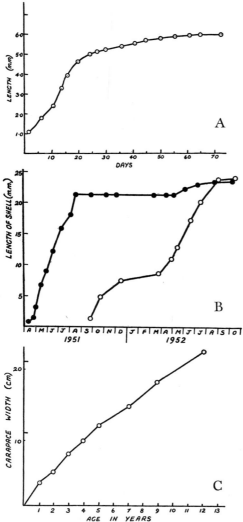

FIG. 31. Growth curves of Crustacea. A, a single female of *Daphnia magna*, reared in the laboratory. B, *Balanus crenatus* (Cirripedia) grown in conditions of continual submergence. Note the stoppage of growth in winter of the specimens settling in April, and the way in which the specimens settling in September catch up with those settling earlier (after Barnes and Powell, 1953). C, *Cancer pagurus* (Decapoda, Brachyura) the edible crab of Europe. (Based on data given by Pearson, 1908).

The actual amount of growth which occurs at each moult varies with the age of the crustacean. Sometimes no growth occurs at all; rarely, as in some individuals of *Daphnia longispina*, a decrease in size is found towards the end of life. By measuring the increase in size at each moult, or by measuring an individual at intervals throughout its life, a curve may be drawn which shows how growth varies during a lifetime. Three examples are given in figs. 31 A-C. It is important to notice the difference in the time scales, and to realise that curves of this sort can be considerably modified by environmental conditions.

The growth of barnacles, once they have settled, presents some interesting differences from the growth of more normal Crustacea. The tough outer shell is not cast off, but is added to at its base, so that the shell increases in height and basal diameter. The more delicate coverings of the limbs and body within the shell are cast off at fairly regular intervals. For instance, a newly settled *Balanus amphritrite niveus* usually moults on the fourth day after settling, and follows this by moulting on the sixth, eighth and tenth days. A total of 19 moults may be passed through during the first 47 days after settling. There does not seem to be any connection between the rate of growth of the outer shell and the moulting cycle.

As in all Crustacea the growth of barnacles is controlled by various environmental factors. One of the most important of these factors is the length of time that the barnacle is left uncovered by the tide. Total submergence appears to be the ideal state for most barnacles, and it is found that their growth rate decreases with increasing duration of exposure to the air. This results in barnacles growing at different rates at different levels on the seashore; those near the top of the shore grow more slowly than those which are lower down and less frequently uncovered.

The rate of flow of water past a barnacle also influences growth. Water currents up to 1·5 knots actually increase the rate of growth, probably by bringing more food within reach. Faster currents cause a decrease in growth rate, and dislodge young barnacles. This is important in relation to barnacle-fouling of ships. If only short stays are made in port there will be very little permanent fouling because the young barnacles are dislodged when the ship starts moving.

There seems to be a certain minimum size, characteristic for each species, which must be reached before a crustacean becomes sexually mature. Thus a female *Daphnia magna* does not reproduce before she reaches a length of 2·1 mm., while a female lobster reaches a length of ten inches before she starts breeding. Maturation is, of course, characterised by an increase in size of the gonads and the production of germ cells. Hormones are believed to control these processes, and experiments indicate that in some species the eyestalks produce a substance which inhibits the growth of the gonads, and that the Y-organ is necessary for sexual maturation, but not necessary for the maintenance of sexual functions once the animal has become mature.

The gonads themselves may act as endocrine organs and produce substances which are necessary for the production of secondary sexual characteristics. The testes of isopods produce such a hormone. In the amphipods there is a special gland on the male duct which seems to be responsible for maintaining the secondary sexual characters of the male. If the gland is removed the male becomes more like the female in general appearance. If an ovary is then implanted into such a male the similarity to a female is more emphasised, and the specimen may develop a brood pouch.

Secondary differences between the sexes take a variety of forms. The antennule of a male *Daphnia* is long and movable, while in the female it is short and fixed (fig. 32). Some male crabs have enormous pincers (fig. 42), while the females remain a more normal shape. The most striking differences are found in parasitic copepods and isopods (chapter 8). The male may be only a minute fraction of the size of the female, and quite different in shape.

The sexes are not always separate; most barnacles are hermaphrodites, but some species have an extra complication. As well as having bisexual individuals they have additional small males which are only a fraction of the size of the hermaphrodites. These complementary males attach themselves inside the mantle cavities of the larger individuals and fertilise the eggs. The possession of male organs by the larger individuals is thought to be an insurance against the failure of the small, short-lived males, which probably cannot feed and have to rely on food stores built up during the free-swimming larval stages.

Some of the Notostraca are also hermaphrodites, and sometimes show an interesting geographical variation in the separation of the sexes. *Triops cancriformis* has both males and females in North Africa, but in Northern Europe only hermaphrodites are found. In these the ovaries have scattered sperm-producing lobes among the developing eggs. The cephalocaridan, *Hutchinsoniella*, is also an hermaphrodite, but its ovaries and testes are quite separate.

A change of sex during the life of an individual is a regular feature in some shrimps. In *Pandalus montagui* some individuals are primarily females, but others begin their lives as males then develop female characteristics after about 13 months, and eggs begin to develop in the reproductive organs. Isopods of the genus *Rhyscotoides* show a similar change, but there seems to be an absence of primary females, all individuals going through a male phase, and it seems probable that some individuals can change back to male after a female phase. The genus is also peculiar in that the female phase retains the male shape of the pleopods.

The normal process of sexual reproduction involves the fusion of a sperm with an egg. The Crustacea offer some exceptions to the general rule, because certain species produce eggs which do not need to be fertilised. *Daphnia* and most other Cladocera provide good examples. In suitable conditions the females produce eggs which give rise to other females without being fertilised; this process may be repeated for hundreds of generations. In poor conditions males appear among the offspring, and some of the females produce eggs which need to be fertilised. These fertilised eggs can withstand adverse conditions, such as drying, and serve to carry the population through periods when environmental conditions are difficult. They are often called resting eggs. Some populations of *Daphnia* can produce resting eggs which are not fertilised, and have completely dispensed with males.

Some of the eggs produced by Anostraca and Conchostraca are peculiar in shape, or have remarkably sculpted surfaces, but the eggs of the majority of Crustacea are unexceptional, being rounded or slightly ovoid. In contrast, the sperms of crustaceans are spectacular in their range of form and size. They may be simple and rounded, as in the Euphausiacea and some Cladocera, or they may have numerous processes radiating from a central body, as in some Decapoda. Sometimes, as in *Argulus*, the sperms look like tadpoles, with a rounded head and a long tail. In the ostracods the most fantastic sperms in the whole animal kingdom are produced. They have long heads and may be up to ten times the length of the male which produced them; further they are longer than those of a whale or an elephant! Lowndes (1935) has suggested that such enormous sperms cannot be functional, and it is a remarkable fact that a great many ostracods are parthenogenetic, producing eggs which do not need to be fertilised.

Sperms are frequently enclosed in a case, the spermatophore, which the male places on the female, generally rather accurately, near the opening of the female ducts.

In many copepods the contents of the spermatophore are extruded by the swelling of some of the sperms, which increase greatly in size and force out the sperms which are actually used to fertilise the eggs.

The sperms of decapods may be contained in a continous tube which is plastered in a coiled mass on to the female, or they may be enclosed in small separate spermatophores, each of which has a stalk by means of which it is attached to a continuous strip. Finally each spermatophore may be quite simple and separated from the others. These three types are typical of the three major groups of the Decapoda, but there are odd exceptions. The first type is found in the Macrura and the dromiid crabs. The second occurs in the Anomura, while the third is found in the Brachyura other than the dromiids. Some intermediate types are produced; the anomuran *Hippa pacifia* makes a spermatophore which consists of a long continuous tube which is attached along its length by means of a ribbon-like stalk to a continuous strip. The macruran *Parribacus antarcticus* produces a continuous tube which becomes twisted so that pockets of sperms are formed, and on further twisting are raised on coiled stalks. The brachyuran spermatophore is not left on the outside of the female, but is passed into a special pocket, the spermatheca, which lies internally at the base of the female duct.

The transfer of the various types of spermatophore, or of free sperms, to the female has the objective of ensuring that the eggs are fertilised. Once fertilisation has taken place the care and attention given to the eggs is variable.

Some Crustacea lay their eggs freely in the water. Certain copepods, such as *Calanus*, some Bathynellacea, Anaspidacea, most Euphausiacea and the penaeid prawns have this habit. Some euphausiids and *Nebalia* carry their eggs between the thoracic limbs, retaining them by means of the setae at the tips of these limbs. The majority of decapods carry their eggs attached to their abdominal appendages, and sometimes, as in *Crangon*, to the last two thoracic limbs. The eggs are attached to special ovigerous setae which have a cement secreted through them. This cement flows over the eggs and binds them to the setae. In some species, such as *Leander squilla*, the ovigerous setae are temporary structures which only appear during the breeding season. The appearance of these setae is probably controlled by hormones produced by the ovary. If *Leander* is castrated, either by infection with the parasitic isopod *Bopyrus* (see p. 115), or by exposure to X-rays, the ovigerous setae are not formed.

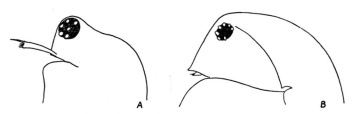

FIG. 32. Sexual dimorphism in the heads of *Daphnia magna*. A, male. B, female.

The details of egg attachment in the decapods vary from family to family, but as a general rule the free-swimming Caridea do not have eggs attached to the last pair of pleopods, and they retain the ability to flex the abdomen. Sudden flexing of the abdomen, producing a backward darting movement, is an important escape movement. The retention of this ability by an egg-bearing female is clearly of survival value to a species.

Most of the Peracarida retain their eggs in a brood pouch formed by plates, or oostegites, which project inwards from the bases of one or more pairs of the walking legs. Some of the Tanaidae have only one pair of oostegites, but up to seven pairs are found in some of the Mysidacea. Deviations from the normal peracaridan brood pouch are found among certain isopods. *Sphaeroma* retains the eggs in pouches which project into the body from the ventral surface.

A unique brood pouch is found in the Thermosbaenacea. These are the only Malacostraca which carry their eggs on their backs, in a pouch formed by the carapace. The female lies on her back when she lays her eggs, and they drop into the pouch.

A dorsal brood pouch, between the body and the carapace, is also found in the Cladocera and Conchostraca; in the latter group there are special processes from some of the limbs which help to keep the eggs in place. The brood pouches of some Cladocera, such as *Moina*, are closed, and there appears to be a nutritive secretion passed into the pouch by the mother. The eggs of *Moina* cannot develop if removed from the brood pouch, whereas the Cladocera with open brood pouches (*Daphnia*, *Chydorus*, etc.) produce eggs which will develop outside the brood pouch, even in distilled water.

Some ostracods also carry their eggs between the body and the carapace, sometimes until hatching, but more usually the eggs are deposited freely in the water, or are attached to plants and stones. In the cirripedes the eggs are retained until hatching in the mantle cavity.

Different locations of the brood pouch are found in the Notostraca and Anostraca. In the Notostraca there is a pouch on the eleventh pair of legs; eggs are laid into this pouch at the beginning of an instar and carried until the animal is ready to moult again. The eggs are then extruded from the pouch and coated with a sticky layer, by means of which they are attached to grass roots and similar objects. The Anostraca carry their eggs in a pouch under the front part of the abdomen. In most species the eggs are carried for an instar and then liberated, still only partly developed and enclosed in a shell. The brine shrimp, *Artemia salina*, is un-usual in that when in favourable conditions it liberates active young from its brood pouch. In other conditions *Artemia* lays eggs, which may develop and hatch rather quickly, but can also lie quiescent for a long period. These eggs are remarkably resistant to adverse conditions; they may be dried and kept for several years and then hatched when put into sea water. They may also be sub-jected to more severe drying by being kept in high vacuum over phosphorus pentoxide, yet they still develop normally when put into sea water. Cooling with liquid air is also survived, and a small proportion of eggs are still viable after being heated to 103° C. for two hours. When these eggs are dry they seem to suspend all activity, and the most refined techniques have failed to reveal any trace of normal respiratory exchange.

The cephalocaridan *Hutchinsoniella* carries two large eggs, each in its own sac suspended from the front of the abdomen.

Those copepods which do not cast their eggs freely into the water carry them in thin-walled sacs suspended from the front of the abdomen. There may be one sac, as in many calanoids and harpacti-coids, or two sacs as in most cyclopoids. Some parasitic copepods, such as the Choniostomatidae (p. 109) produce up to six or eight egg sacs.

The young crustacean which emerges from the egg may resemble its parent rather closely, but more usually it is very different, and has to go through a series of larval stages before attaining the adult form. The nauplius is a very characteristic crustacean larva. Three nauplii belonging to different groups are shown in fig. 33. The main features which they possess in common are a simple non-segmented body and three pairs of appendages: the antennules, antennae and mandibles. When the body is elongated and seg-mented the nauplius becomes a metanauplius. The great interest attached to the nauplius is due to its occurrence during the develop-ment of so many different groups of the Crustacea. A nauplius or metanauplius is found in at least one representative of each of the following groups: Notostraca, Anostraca, Conchostraca, Cladocera (from the winter egg of *Leptodora* only), Copepoda, Cirripedia, Euphausiacea, and the penaeid prawns. In addition the embryos of many of the other groups go through a stage which is very similar to a nauplius while still within the egg.

The stage following the nauplius varies in the different groups. There may be a gradual change through a number of moults

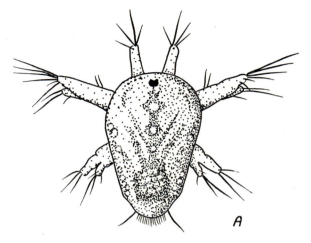

FIG. 33. A, first nauplius of *Cyclops fuscus* (Copepoda), dorsal view.

towards the adult form, as found in the Notostraca and Anostraca (figs. 34A-B) or there may be a number of very different stages involved.

The nauplius of a copepod, such as *Calanus*, may moult five times, still retaining the nauplius form. At the next moult it will change into a copepodid, which is similar to the adult, except that it is not sexually mature, and the limbs are not fully developed.

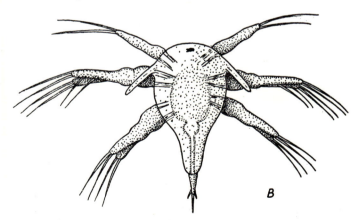

FIG. 33. B, newly hatched nauplius of *Balanus* (Cirripedia), dorsal view.

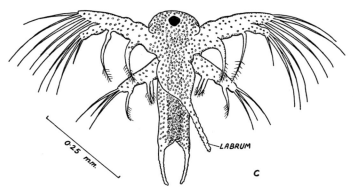

FIG. 33. C, Metanauplius of *Limnadia lenticularis* (Conchostraca, ventral view. Note the enormous labrum.

The copepodid moults five times before attaining maturity. The parasitic copepods often have highly modified life histories—some of these are dealt with in chapter 8.

In the cirripedes the nauplius is followed by the cypris (fig. 35). This larva has the carapace extending down the sides of the body so that the creature looks superficially like an ostracod. When it is examined carefully it is seen to be very different from an ostracod, particularly in the number of limbs. It is the cypris which attaches to a solid object and changes into the adult.

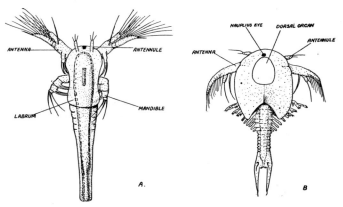

FIG. 34 A, Metanauplius of *Artemia salina* (Anostraca), ventral view. Note the elongated body and the absence of limbs on the thorax. B, Young *Triops cancriformis*, the nauplius stage has been passed and the carapace developed to look like the adult, but the creature still swims with the large antennae, even though the thoracic limbs are developing. Compare with figs. 5 and 19.

The antennules of the cypris larva are relatively large, and project in front of the carapace; a cement gland opens on the third segment and serves for attachment of the larva. Once attached there are changes in the proportions of various parts of the body (fig. 35). The thorax is bent back so that it comes to lie across the longitudinal axis of the carapace. If the barnacle is one with a stalk there is a great increase in length in the region in front of the mouth, but the mouth has meanwhile been bent away from the point of attachment. The thoracic legs become longer and beset with fine hairs in readiness for the adoption of the adult method

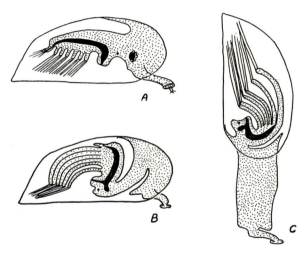

FIG. 35. Metamorphosis of a stalked barnacle. A, Cypris attaching by means of its large antennule. B, reorientation of the body within the carapace. C, growth of the pre-oral region of head and assumption of adult form. (from Calman, after Korschelt and Heider).

of feeding (see p. 24). Calcareous plates are formed in the carapace; the details of the arrangements of these plates varies from one genus to another. In *Lepas* the carapace retains more or less the cypris shape, while in stalkless barnacles the cypris carapace is lost and a new carapace is developed to encircle the body. With the development of calcareous plates the barnacle assumes its adult form and spends the rest of its life attached to the place it selected as a cypris. It is clear that the selection of a settling place by a cypris is an important event in the life of a barnacle. Experiments have shown that many species settle gregariously. A cypris prefers to settle in a place already inhabited by others of its own species. If a cypris cannot find such a place it can delay the change into adult form for at least two weeks. The aggregation of barnacles in this way is an obvious aid to reproduction; if barnacles lived in isolation the chances of the eggs becoming fertilised would be very small, for although most barnacles are hermaphrodite they mostly cross fertilise. Because of their immobile adult state the search for possible reproductive partners has shifted to the larval stage.

The position taken up by a cypris in relation to water currents is also important. The feeding mechanism is most effective when the legs beat into a current; the cypris should therefore orientate so that this will be possible when the adult form is assumed. In fact it is found that the cypris tends to align itself with respect to light, and this factor overrides all others to such an extent that a cypris sometimes settles in a position which is disadvantageous with respect to a water current. This can be corrected to some extent by the adult barnacle twisting during its growth. In situations where barnacles are exposed to a current from one direction, for instance on a boat moored at one end, the adults become orientated in such a way that the feeding limbs beat into the current.

The life history of a malacostracan may be long and complicated, or the creature emerging from the egg may resemble the parents so closely that all it has to do is to grow and become mature. This direct type of development is found throughout the Peracarida, Syncarida, Leptostraca and some of the Decapoda, particularly those crayfish and crabs which live in fresh water.

A full sequence of larval forms is found in the Euphausiacea; a nauplius emerges from the egg, changes to a metanauplius, and this develops a carapace and becomes longer in the trunk to form a calyptopsis larva. This has paired eyes, but they are not freely movable. When the eyes become stalked and movable, and the pleopods have developed, the larva is called a furcilia. Later, as the adult form is more closely approached the larva is called a cyrtopia. The names of these larval forms were given at a time when they were thought to belong to distinct genera, and before it was realised that they all formed part of the developmental series of one type of crustacean.

The various stages of the Euphausiacea have their counterparts in the development of the penaeid prawns. These also hatch as a nauplius, change to a metanauplius, then go through stages called protozoea, zoea and a post-larval stage which is very similar to the adult. The main diagnostic features of the various larval types are connected with the stage of development of the various limbs and their use in locomotion. The nauplius swims by means of its antennae, and so does the protozoea, the zoea uses its thoracic limbs for swimming, while the post-larval stage uses the abdominal limbs, as does the adult penaeid. It is unfortunate that different names were given to the stages of the Euphausiacea and the penaeids, because it is now clear that the calyptopsis is a protozoea, and the furcilia a zoea, while the cyrtopia can be regarded as the first post-larval stage.

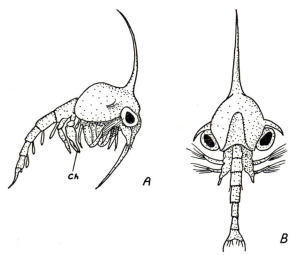

FIG. 36. Larvae of Crabs. A, late zoea, in side view, note the chela already present. B, the same zoea viewed from behind to show the way in which the stalked eyes protrude and give an all round view.

Most of the decapods miss out the naupliar stages and hatch as a zoea, which may sometimes be heavily ornamented with spines. The zoea of a crab (fig. 36A-B) changes into a megalopa (fig. 36c), which is just like a little crab with its tail extended behind it. The equivalent stage of a hermit crab is called a glaucothoe.

Peculiar larvae are produced by the Palinura. The body of the larva is flattened and leaf-like (fig. 37), so that the name phyllosoma has been given to it. Recent work has shown that the California spiny lobster, *Panulirus interruptus*, goes through eleven phyllosoma stages, then changes into a small lobster-like creature with long

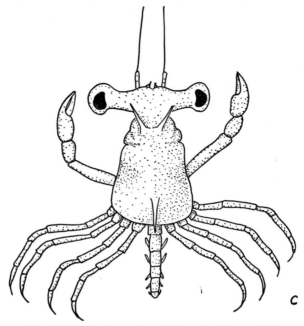

FIG. 36. C, Megalopa of a spider crab (*Macropodia*).

antennae, known as a puerulus; this gradually assumes the adult form.

Further multiplication of names of larval stages has occurred in the Stomatopoda. The stage at which hatching occurs is variable. In some genera, such as *Coronida*, the egg gives rise to an antizoea, which does not have stalked eyes in the first instar, and the abdomen is not divided into segments. The abdominal segments become progressively defined through several instars. In other genera, such as *Squilla*, a pseudozoea hatches from the egg. This is in some ways more advanced than the antizoea, and has the abdomen divided into segments bearing rudimentary appendages, but the appendages on the thorax are not so well developed. The change to the adult form is gradual, without any abrupt transitions.

In the accounts of the various larval forms and their succession during the life history of the individual we have not related the sequence to seasons or years. It would be impossible to generalise, even for one small group. In the following pages some examples are given of types of seasonal reproductive cycles and an attempt is made to relate them to the environmental conditions in which the animals live.

An annual cycle may be made up of several generations, none of which survives for more than a fraction of a year; it may be performed by individuals which live a little more than a year, or it may involve individuals which survive for several years, but have regular annual movements and breeding periods. Variation in the details of such cycles can be immense; only a few examples can be studied here.

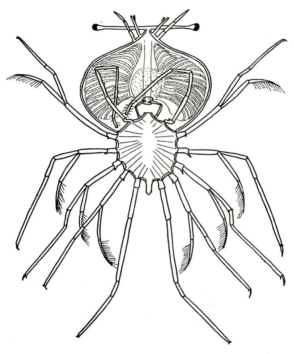

Fig. 37. Phyllosoma larva of *Jassus* (Decapoda Reptantia, Palinura).

The annual cycle of *Daphnia magna* in a temperate climate is a good example of the first of the three main types. The population overwinters as resting eggs, or as females which grow slowly and reproduce very little. In the spring the resting eggs hatch, and the females begin to reproduce more rapidly as the temperature of the water rises and small algae increase to provide more food. As we

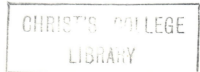

have already mentioned, the young which are produced by the resting eggs are all females, which lay eggs not requiring fertilisation and give rise to more females. The population increases rapidly. A mature female can produce over a hundred live young every three days, and each of these young matures within a fortnight, cr even less than a week when the water is warm enough. When a certain density has been reached the effects of crowding make themselves felt, and some of the eggs develop into males. Some of the females then produce resting eggs. The population often diminishes after this due to deaths from overcrowding and food shortage. Towards the end of the summer the small algae in the pond begin to increase again so that more food becomes available to the water flea. The population again increases rapidly until crowding effects intervene once more; males and resting eggs appear again, and the population dies down or disappears, leaving only resting eggs to overwinter.

This cycle has been described in terms of the population, no one individual survives for the whole year. It has been found that the length of life of *Daphnia magna* varies with temperature, it can live for 108 days at 8° C., but only 29 days at 28° C. Some of the females which overwinter may live for about six months. It has also been found experimentally that females grow to a larger size at low temperatures, although they grow more slowly. This fits in with what is found in nature; the largest specimens are found at the end of the winter, and when these individuals die there is a marked

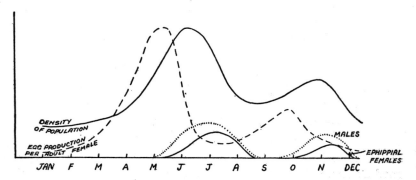

FIG. 38. An idealised diagram of the yearly cycle of *Daphnia magna* in temperate Europe. The precise location of the peaks is not important—they vary from year to year according to the weather. Variations from pond to pond also occur. Sometimes the population does not diminish in summer, sometimes it may disappear. Notice the coincidence of the onset of sexual reproduction with periods of maximum population.

PLATE I

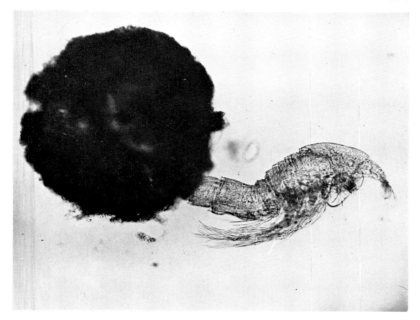

(*Photograph by V. N. Casey*)

Canthocamptus staphylinus (Copepoda, Harpacticoida) emerging from its cyst. This species is most abundant and active in the winter. In the summer it forms cysts in which it rests through periods of high temperatures and low oxygen concentrations. This specimen is from the Lago Maggiori, N. Italy, found by Dr. O. Ravera.

PLATE II

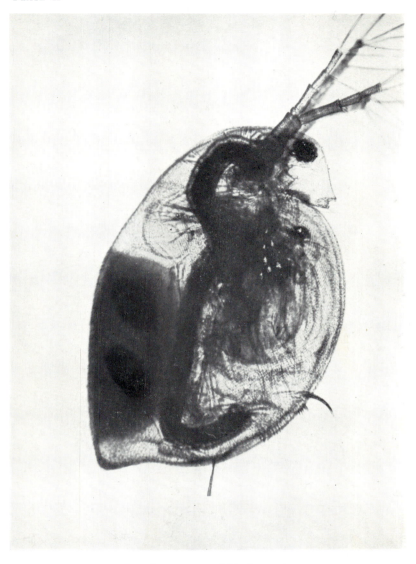

Daphnia magna (Cladocera)

A female with a modified darkened brood pouch, or ephippium, containing two resting eggs. The heart is inside above the brood pouch. Actual length of the body.

drop in the average size of mature females. A diagrammatic inter-
pretation of this cycle is given in fig. 38. The cycle is not always so
straightforward, because ponds are complicated and variable places.
It is easy enough to find populations which have outbursts of sexual
reproduction, involving the appearance of males and resting eggs,
at intervals throughout the summer.

The brackish water isopod *Sphaeroma hookeri* lives for about a
year and a half. The annual cycle of this species near Kiel has
been described by Kinne (1954). Most of the young are born in the
period from June to the end of August, and two broods can be
distinguished. The first brood is laid into the mothers' internal
pouches in May and emerges at the end of June or the beginning
of July. The second brood emerges late in August, with stragglers
as late as November. This second brood is produced by females
born in the first brood, so that sexual maturity is reached in a
matter of a month or so. After producing a brood a female moults
and does not produce any more young until the next year. In this
way the first brood of each year is produced by year-old females,
and the second brood by month-old females. All the females do
not mature so quickly, about three-quarters of them only produce
their first young the year after they were born. The annual cycle
seems to vary with latitude; Jensen (1955) found that in the South
Harbour of Copenhagen only one really effective brood is produced
each year. This brood is liberated a little later than the first brood
at Kiel. The year-old females which produce this brood then moult,
losing their brood pouches, but they regain them in August and lay
another brood of eggs. Only a small percentage of the females suc-
ceed in rearing their second brood. At Copenhagen there does not
seem to be any maturation of females in the summer of their
birth. This contrast with the population at Kiel is probably due to
the lower temperature in spring at the Danish capital.

The common shrimp, *Crangon vulgaris*, serves as the example of
the third type of annual cycle. The account which follows is based
on the study made by Lloyd and Yonge (1947) in the Bristol
Channel and Severn Estuary. Females live for four or perhaps five
years, while the males live for about three years. During the winter
the population migrates out of the less saline waters of the estuary,
but returns in the spring. The breeding season in the estuary
extends from March to June. This is a shorter season than that
found further out in the Bristol Channel, where breeding occurs
from January to August. Winter breeding in the estuary is pre-

G

82 A BIOLOGY OF CRUSTACEA

vented by the combined effects of low temperature and low salinity, for the shrimp can only withstand reduced salinities when the water is reasonably warm. The breeding season in the estuary is only long enough to allow the production of a single brood, but in the Channel the season allows the production of two broods. Females in the estuary do not produce a brood until their third year, while those in the Channel produce a brood in their second year and two broods in each of their third and fourth years. The more exacting conditions of life in the estuary thus influence the reproductive cycle in two ways. The breeding season is shortened and the onset of maturity is delayed.

The three examples of annual cycles show how each species has its own particular breeding season and how each is modified by variations in the environment. In *Daphnia* the availability of algae and the density of the population are important; in *Sphaeroma* the cycle is influenced greatly by the temperature in spring, while in *Crangon* the combined effects of temperature and salinity reduce breeding activity in estuaries.

LITERATURE

BARNES, H., & POWELL, H. T. (1953). The growth of *Balanus balanoides* (L.) and *B. crenatus* Brug. under varying conditions of submersion. *J. mar. Biol. Ass. U.K.* 32: 107-127.

BERG, K. (1934). Cyclic reproduction, sex determination and depression in the Cladocera. *Biol. Rev.* 9: 139-174.

CARLISLE, D. B. (1957). On the hormonal inhibition of moulting in decapod Crustacea. II. The terminal anecdysis in Crabs. *J. mar. Biol. Ass. U.K.* 36: 291-307.

COSTLOW, J. D., & BOOKHOUT, C. G. (1957). Body growth versus shell growth in *Balanus improvisus*. *Biol. Bull., Wood's Hole* 113: 224-232.

CRISP, D. J., & STUBBINGS, H. G. (1957). The orientation of barnacles to water currents. *J. anim. Ecol.* 26: 179-196.

GREEN, J. (1956). Growth, size and reproduction in *Daphnia* (Crustacea: Cladocera). *Proc. zool. Soc. Lond.* 126: 173-204.

GURNEY, R. (1942). *Larvae of decapod Crustacea.* London, Ray Society. pp. 1-306.

JENSEN, J. P. (1955). Biological observations on the isopod *Sphaeroma hookeri*. Leach. *Vidensk. Medd. fra Dansk naturh. Foren.* 117: 305-339.

KINNE, O. (1954). Eidonomie, Anatomie und Lebenszyklus von *Sphaeroma hookeri* Leach (Isopoda). *Kiel. Meeresforsch.* 10: 100-120.

LLOYD, A. J., & YONGE, C. M. (1947). The biology of *Crangon vulgaris* L. in the Bristol Channel and Severn Estuary. *J. mar. Biol. Ass. U.K.* 26: 626-661.

LONGHURST, A. R. (1955). The reproduction and cytology of the Notostraca (Crustacea, Phyllopoda). *Proc. zool. Soc. Lond.* 125: 671-680.

LOWNDES, A. G. (1935). The sperms of freshwater ostracods. *Proc. zool. Soc. Lond.* 1935, i. 35-48.

MATTHEWS, D. C. (1956). The origin of the spermatophoric mass of the sand crab *Hippa pacifia*. *Quart. J. micr. Sci.* 97: 257-268.

YONGE, C. M. (1955). Egg attachment in *Crangon vulgaris* and other Caridea. *Proc. roy. Soc. Edinb.* B. 65: 369-400.

CHAPTER VI

BEHAVIOUR

B E H A V I O U R can be defined in its widest sense as any change in activity made by the intact animal. This rules out the responses of isolated parts in physiological preparations, though such preparations can play a part in the analysis of behaviour. However, behaviour is fundamentally a characteristic of the whole animal, and is usually more than the sum of its physiological mechanisms. The additional 'something' is gained by the integration and co-ordination, often coupled with mutual inhibitions, of these mechanisms to form the complicated mechanism of the whole animal.

Our definition has been made purposely wide so that almost any change of activity can be included. Even the adoption of a posture is an active process involving reactions to various features of the environment. A change of posture is clearly a part of behaviour.

Before we deal with complicated behaviour patterns it will be as well to try to find out the extent to which a crustacean is aware of its environment. How much can it see? Can it hear, or feel, or smell? These questions can be answered with varying degrees of completeness, and the answers depend on how much we know about the structure and functioning of the various sense organs which the Crustacea possess.

The most conspicuous of these organs are the eyes. In a typical decapod each eye consists of several hundred tubular units radiating from the end of the optic nerve. Each of these units is a miniature eye (fig. 39). There is a central optical tract, with a crystalline cone and a crystalline tract at its base leading to a group of cells known as the retinulae. Sometimes the crystalline cone abuts directly on the retinulae, without any intervening crystalline tract. Each tubular element is isolated from the others, to a greater or lesser extent, by two groups of pigment cells; one group (distal) around the crystalline cone, the other group (proximal) is arranged around the retinulae. Both groups of pigment cells can cause their dark pigments to move and cover varying amounts of the tubular eye.

84

The picture built up in a compound eye of this sort is a mosaic of light and dark spots, each perceived by an individual element. The visual acuity of several Crustacea has been tested by placing them in a round dish, then rotating a pattern of stripes around the dish and finding the finest stripes that the creature responds to, either by swimming in an attempt to keep the same position in relation to a particular group of stripes, or by movements of its eyes showing that it is seeing the stripes as they move past. In this way it has been found that the visual acuity is greatest when the proximal pigment is expanded around the retinulae. This is probably effective

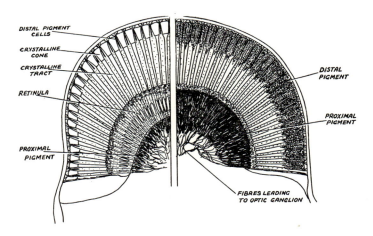

FIG. 39. Diagrammatic section through the eye of a crayfish. The right side is shown in the light adapted state, and is drawn from a thicker section than the left side which is in the dark adapted condition.

in reducing stray reflexions from the back of the eye. The distal pigment does not seem to have much effect on visual acuity, but it may be useful in decreasing the sensitivity of the eye in bright light.

There is some evidence that crabs and lobsters use their eyes when hunting, and can see quite well. One striking example was found during some experiments on hermit crabs. These were being kept in artificial shells made of glass, so that the soft, succulent-looking abdomen was visible. A starved *Portunus puber*, a most pugnacious crab, which was in the same aquarium, made violent attempts to attack the abdomen through the shell, clearly indicating that it could see the vulnerable abdomen of the hermit.

Some Crustacea can distinguish between various colours. This is perhaps best shown in *Hippolyte varians*, whose choice of a matching background has already been described (p. 51). Responses to light of different colours are also shown by *Daphnia*: in red light most of the individuals 'dance' more or less upright in the water, and do not move about much in a horizontal plane. Under blue light most individuals tend to swim horizontally. This behaviour is not constant, because the responses can be over-ruled by hunger; starved *Daphnia* swim horizontally no matter what the colour of the light may be. When abundant food is available the water fleas perform their red dance even in blue light.

These reactions are clearly an aid to keeping *Daphnia* in an area rich in planktonic green algae, which form its main food. The light transmitted by such algae has had most of the blue removed, so that the water fleas will do their red dance in such areas, and not move much in a horizontal direction. The change to horizontal swimming in blue light helps the creatures to explore a wide area when food is sparse.

Perhaps the most remarkable feature of crustacean behaviour is the diurnal migration which many of the planktonic species undergo. In its typical form this consists of a movement towards the surface at dusk, a slow irregular downward movement during the night, movement up again towards the surface at dawn, and a marked movement away from the surface as the sun becomes brighter. In some species it has been shown that light intensity is the main governing factor, and in *Daphnia magna* two distinct mechanisms have been found. One mechanism is mediated by the compound eye, and involves swimming away from intense light and towards dim light. The direction of the light is important in this response. If *D. magna* is lit from below it can be made to swim upwards towards the surface by a bright light, thus reversing the usual sequence in Nature. The other mechanism does not involve the compound eye, but may involve the ocellus. This second mechanism is not related to the direction of the light, but to its intensity. As light intensity increases from darkness there is at first an increase in swimming rate, but when the light becomes brighter swimming activity is decreased. If specimens of *D. magna* have the compound eyes removed, and are then lit from below, they sink downwards in bright light. Their responses are identical with those of eyeless animals lit from above, and in marked contrast with the responses of intact animals. The reactions of the eyeless specimens account for the dawn rise to the surface. As the light gradually increases they swim upwards, then when the light becomes strong enough to inhibit swimming they sink down again. Other experiments have shown that the colour of the light is important in these responses. If the spectrum of the light is shifted towards the blue, without any change in intensity it provokes active down-swimming; shifting the spectrum towards the red, again without change in intensity, can provoke up-swimming. In general, *Daphnia* is much more sensitive to changes in the blue part of the spectrum than in the red.

Although the action of light is so clear it is by no means the only factor involved. Changes in temperature can alter the strength of the response to light. Dissolved carbon dioxide and other substances can also influence such responses. The first experiment demonstrating this is reputed to be the occasion when the celebrated biologist Loeb poured beer into his tanks of *Daphnia* and found that it reversed their responses to light.

Several Crustacea, such as the isopod *Eurydice pulchra*, and larvae of the crabs *Portunus* and *Carcinus* are sensitive to changes in pressure; they swim upwards when pressure is increased.

The general impression gained from the various studies on vertical migration is that the major features are controlled by light intensity, but the details and fine adjustments are controlled by other factors such as temperature, pressure and dissolved carbon dioxide.

Vertical migration in the sea can be very considerable; some euphausiids migrate 200 metres up and down each day. A migration of this magnitude can carry a crustacean into a layer of water which is moving in a different direction from the one in which it started, and it is thought that it may gain certain advantages from this. Instead of drifting in one direction in a limited patch of water the crustacean can change direction and sample a greater volume of its environment. This may well be important if food becomes scarce; if the crustacean drifted along in the same patch all the time it might starve, but by migrating to a lower level moving in another direction it can then come up again in a fresh patch which may be richer in food.

Apart from such advantages the downward migration during the day may be essential for some species, at least at some seasons. It has for instance been shown that the copepod *Calanus finmarchicus* is killed by prolonged exposure to bright sunlight. If this is so why do not the Crustacea stay permanently in the lower layers? The answer to this lies in the fact that it is in the upper layers of the sea that food, in the form of minute planktonic plants, is most abundant. It has been suggested that vertical migration is controlled by feeding reactions. The crustaceans come up at night and feed, then sink down when full, but a creature like *Daphnia* can fill its gut in half an hour when food is abundant, and empty it just as quickly. The time scale of such events is of the wrong order to be a dominant factor in controlling diurnal migration. Nevertheless starvation can act as one of the fine adjustments in the whole complex; *Daphnia* tends to swim towards a light more when starved than when it is well fed.

One of the simplest reactions to light is that known as the dorsal light reaction. A free-swimming crustacean, such as *Triops*, normally keeps its back upwards towards the light. If a light is placed below it, the creature turns over and swims back downwards. A prawn, *Processa caniculata*, behaves in a similar manner.

Triops keeps its body on an even keel by balancing the light received by the two compound eyes. If one of these is painted over the creature swims in spirals, rolling over towards the functional eye. The change to swimming upside down when lit from below is started by the small median eye, which has a window through to the underside of the head. Once *Triops* has turned over the two compound eyes take over to maintain its balance.

Artemia salina reacts to light in precisely the opposite way. The normal swimming position is with the back downwards. If lit from below it rolls or somersaults into the reverse position.

As well as keeping their back to the light most Crustacea keep their bellies towards the earth; they lie across the pull of gravity. The organs which tell a crustacean which way up it is are called statocysts, and are usually found near the base of the antennules. Statocysts are relatively simple in structure, usually just a rounded sac lined with special sense cells which often have hair-like projections from their surfaces. One or more small stone-like structures, the statoliths, lie inside the sac. The statoliths will naturally always fall downwards towards the earth and will press on different groups of cells according to the position that the crustacean takes up with respect to gravity. The impulses set up by the movements of the statoliths are relayed to the brain, and the crustacean is thus aware of its position in relation to the pull of gravity.

In some prawns the place of the statolith is taken by small sand grains, which are placed in the statocyst by the prawn after it has moulted. This allows an interesting experiment. If iron filings are offered to the prawn it uses them instead of sand grains. It is then possible to make the prawn turn upside down by placing a magnet above it.

In some species, such as the crayfish, *Potamobius*, it seem that two statocysts are necessary for the creature to maintain its balance. If one is removed and the body is held in its normal position with respect to gravity the crayfish acts as if it is tilted towards the intact side, and pushes with the legs of that side as if to right itself. *Leander xiphias* seems able to manage with just one statocyst; its balance is not disturbed when one is removed.

Normally a crustacean will be subjected to light from above and the pull of gravity from below. What happens if the two stimuli are in opposition? In those species with statocysts the pull of gravity takes precedence. Although lit from below a prawn such as *Leander* will remain standing in its normal position. If its statocysts are removed it will then turn its back towards the light. We have already seen that *Processa caniculata* performs a dorsal light reaction when it is intact; this is because it has no statocysts; this is also true of the other Crustacea which show a dorsal light reaction when intact.

A statocyst can also give information about the rate of turning when a crab changes direction. In the statocysts of crabs there are two types of hair-like processes coming from the sense cells. One type is hooked and is frequently in contact with the numerous minute statoliths; this type gives information about the position of the body in relation to gravity. The other type of hair is long and straight, projecting into the fluid within the statocyst. These hairs are affected by the movement of the fluid when the crab turns, and the sense cells from which they arise relay information to the brain.

There is also evidence that crabs can hear, at least in the wide sense of the term hearing. Pumphrey (1950) has defined hearing in the following way. "An animal hears when it behaves as if it has located a moving object (a sound source) not in contact with it." Experiments to demonstrate hearing ability must of course be designed to exclude the possibility of other senses locating the object first. It has been shown that mysids are sensitive to sounds in water, and that they are less sensitive when their statocysts have been removed. The mysidacean statocyst is peculiar because it is located in the tail (fig. 40), while in the decapods the statocysts are found at the bases of the antennules.

Additional evidence that decapods can hear is derived from the fact that a considerable number of species have special devices for producing sound. The spiny lobsters (*Palinurus* and *Panulirus*) produce sounds by rasping the bases of their antennae against a toothed ridge on the carapace. Two main sounds are produced by *Panulirus*

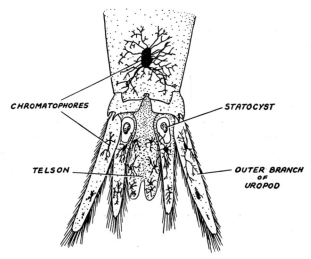

FIG. 40. Tail of a mysidacean (*Macromysis*) to show the statocysts on the inner branches of the uropods.

argus: one is a sharp rasp, which is accompanied by violent contractions of the abdomen. This is clearly a defensive sound emitted when the creature is attacked and is attempting to escape. The other sound is a slow rattle which is emitted when the spiny lobsters are in groups. The function of this sound is unknown, but the fact that it is emitted by undisturbed lobsters when in the presence of others suggests that it is for their benefit and that they have some means of perceiving it.

Some crabs of the genus *Uca* make rasping noises if another crab looks into their burrow. Such a noise is regarded as a sign that the burrow is occupied, and as such it is usually respected, indicating that the sound has been perceived by the exploring crab.

Another set of sense organs is concerned with giving a crustacean information about the disposition of its parts. It is always useful to know what position one's abdomen is in, or where one's legs are without having to look for them. This information is provided by nerve cells which are situated on or supply processes to special small strands which are stretched to varying extents when the main muscles contract.

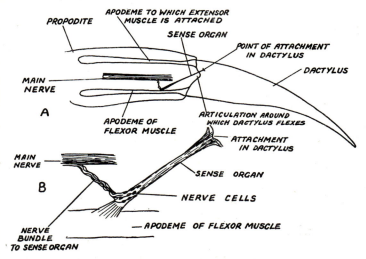

Fig. 41. Diagram of a sense organ near the end of a leg of the shore crab *Carcinus maenas*. A shows the general arrangement. B shows the details, including the nerve cells which perceive changes in the length of the organ according to the position of the dactylus. The apodemes are prolongations from the skeleton of the dactylus which serve for the attachment of muscles. (After Burke, 1954.)

One such organ is found near the end of the legs of the shore crab, *Carcinus maenas* (fig. 41). This is arranged so that when the dactylus is flexed the organ is stretched and the nerve cells in the propodite relay information to the central nervous system. Other stretch receptors are found in the muscles which run from the thorax to the abdomen in lobsters and prawns. These receptors are modified muscles, often very thin, with a number of nerve cells supplying them.

Similar structures have been found at the bases of the legs in several different decapods. In the lobster there is in addition a second organ running close to the modified muscle, but not apparently formed from muscle. Instead the second organ appears to consist of a tube of elastic fibres with a row of nerve cells inside it. Recent work by Alexandrowicz (1958) suggests that one organ may be concerned with registering forward movements and the other with registering backward movements of the leg. Other types of nerve cells, the N-cells, have been found on the surfaces of ordinary muscles in the thorax of lobsters and prawns; their function is unknown, but they presumably gather some sort of information about the state of the muscles.

Crustacea also have a well-developed sense of touch. This may seem surprising for a creature with a hard outer skeleton, but the numerous setae over the surface of the body are supplied with nerves and any deflection is relayed to the central nervous system.

A sense of smell, which is the ability to perceive chemical substances, is also present. Specially modified setae, with very thin walls to allow diffusion of substances to the sense cells, are found particularly on the antennules, antennae and mouthparts. Perhaps the setae on the mouthparts are more concerned with what we call taste, but it is difficult to distinguish between taste and smell in a creature like a crab; it is better to use the general term chemoreception, which covers both. Experiments have shown that crabs can respond to incredibly low concentrations of substances like vanilla and acetic acid.

The Crustacea are thus well aware of several important features in their environment, and have a knowledge of their position with respect to light and gravity, and of the disposition of their parts when they adopt any particular posture.

A particular posture is often adopted for a particular purpose. We have already seen (p. 51) how the land crab *Sesarma meinerti* adopts a pugnacious attitude to back up its warning coloration. Another posture is adopted by the spider crab *Hyas coarctatus* This species hides among seaweeds, but its claws, each of which has a conspicuous pink patch, are waved gently in the water to attract small fishes. When these come near enough they are captured and eaten.

Posturing of a different type is seen in the courtship displays of fiddler crabs. These crabs belong to the large genus *Uca* which contains many species with brightly coloured males. The males have one chela enormously enlarged in comparison with the other (fig.

42), and often coloured in contrast with the rest of the body. Two typical examples of brilliant male coloration are *U. batuenta* and *U. beebi*: the former has a white-speckled, golden-brown carapace and the chela is pure white, dazzling and polished, the latter has the front part of the carapace brilliant iridescent green, part of the large limb is bright ochre or rosy pink and the fingers of the chela are white. These descriptions apply to displaying males, when otherwise engaged they are not so bright.

The display is usually directed towards a female near at hand, and consists of waving the large chela in a manner which is

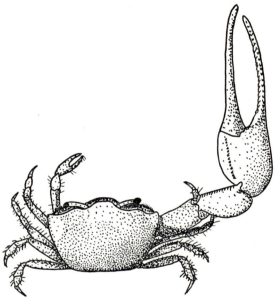

Fig. 42. Male of *Uca pugilator*.

characteristic for each species. *Uca batuenta* raps its chela smartly three or four times on the ground; *U. oerstedi* stretches its chela outwards and upwards, and while it is fully extended the front legs are vibrated rapidly, displaying brilliant blue patches.

The males may spend many hours displaying to females which show no reaction to their antics, but eventually a female will follow a displaying male into its burrow or mate with it on the surface of the sand. There is no evidence of sexual selection in the sense of a female choosing the brightest or most active male, but the characteristic display and coloration indicate to a female the presence, in a breeding condition, of a male of her own species.

There is a great multiplicity of activities in which Crustacea indulge, but we cannot deal with them all here. Many are mentioned in the writings of the great naturalists, particularly Darwin. In general we can say that these activities are directed towards the crustacean's own well-being: they have their special escape movements, such as the violent flexing of the abdomen in the crayfish, or the rapid darting of *Cyclops*—a most successful procedure, as anyone who has tried to catch these copepods with a pipette will know. They have maintenance activities, such as burrowing, cleaning their limbs, and feeding; these activities are diversified and adapted to the particular set of conditions in which a species lives.

It is not much use an animal being adapted to live in a particular set of conditions if it does not behave in such a way as to keep it in those conditions. From this point of view the behaviour of an animal is one of the most important features of its relationship with its environment. The Crustacea provide a wide range of complexity of behaviour, and examples can be chosen to show how the behaviour of a species is related to its survival and to the particular set of conditions in which it is best suited to live. The woodlice are probably the best of these examples.

Woodlice live in damp places, and have a remarkably simple behavioural mechanism for keeping them in such places. They tend to stay still more often in damp situations than in dry ones, and they walk more quickly in dry places than in damp ones. This means that as soon as a woodlouse enters a dry area it begins to walk more quickly, but when a damp area is found the woodlouse may stop, or at least walk more slowly. Clearly in this way they will aggregate in damp places. No directional response is needed, it is merely a matter of increased locomotory activity in dry conditions. This simple mechanism is a life saver, because a woodlouse, such as *Porcellio*, dies in about six hours in dry air.

There are, of course, other factors in the life of a woodlouse. The normal reaction to light is for the woodlouse to move away from it; this tends to lead it to dark, damp places. But what if the dark place becomes dry, can the woodlouse overcome its negative reaction towards the light and move out before it dies of desiccation? In fact, a woodlouse becomes attracted towards the light when suffering from desiccation. This, at first sight, seems suicidal, but the creature retains its responses to dampness, and slows down or stops when it comes to a damp place. Once it gets over the effects of desiccation it becomes photo-negative again and moves away from the light.

These simple responses are closely linked with a woodlouse's way of life. It spends the day hiding in dark, damp places, but at night it comes out and walks about. The negative reaction to light makes sure that it gets under cover before daybreak, so avoiding possible daytime predators. The positive reaction to light develops in emergencies, when the daytime hiding-place dries up. The only thing that these reactions do not explain is why the woodlouse walks about at night; they do explain why it does not normally walk about during the day.

The nocturnal wanderings of woodlice are due to an innate tendency to activity at night, which, once begun, is not prevented by the creatures responses to humidity and light. The night is dark, and usually much more humid than the day. Coupled with this it has been found by experiment that the tendency to stay still in damp places is not so strong after the animals have been in the dark for some time.

It would be a mistake to suppose that all woodlice have identical reactions to humidity and light. The account given above applies to *Oniscus* and *Porcellio*. The pill-woodlouse, *Armadillidium vulgare*, is rather more resistant to desiccation than most other woodlice, and can often be seen walking about in bright sunlight, particularly in the morning.

It is probable that most other Crustacea have a similar series of responses, though they are almost certainly related to other features of their environments. They have not been analysed in the same detail as the responses of woodlice, but they undoubtedly result in the creatures being kept in the conditions which suit them best.

The responses of woodlice to light and humidity are almost mechanical, no element of learning is involved. By the very nature of the dangers to which it is exposed a woodlouse cannot benefit from learning that it will die if exposed to dry air for too long; there can be no benefit from previous experience. But there are situations which present crustaceans with the opportunity of learning, and some at least are capable of benefiting from it.

The simplest form of learning is that known as habitation. This process involves the dropping of responses to stimuli that experience has shown to be harmless. If a jam-jar containing *Daphnia* is shaken gently all the individuals swim rapidly downwards as if to escape. When the jar is allowed to stand still for a while the water fleas gradually swim upwards again and occupy all the water. A further shaking sends them scurrying downwards again, but it is noticeable that a few continue swimming more or less normally. If this is repeated at regular intervals, with about the same degree of shaking, the response wanes, and very few individuals swim downwards when the jar is shaken. This might be interpreted as a form of fatigue, but the response reappears if the shaking is made more violent, or if the creatures are stirred around with a glass rod.

Habituation is very necessary in the natural world. If an animal responded to all the possible danger signals it would rapidly become neurotic and would have no time for feeding or other activities.

Crustacea also show more complex types of learning. *Asellus aquaticus* can be taught to choose between a left or a right turn in a simple T-shaped maze. The training involves punishment when the wrong turn is taken; this need not be severe, a light touch from a paint brush is sufficient. Woodlice can go one better and choose between an upper and a lower path, a feat that *Asellus* seems incapable of learning. Crabs and lobsters can be taught mazes with several turns.

It has been claimed by one worker that *Daphnia* can be taught to swim through a tube towards the light, but other workers have found no signs of such ability in the Cladocera.

Another type of learning is shown by crabs when kept in aquaria; they quickly learn that the appearance of a person is associated with feeding time, and they emerge from their hiding places in attitudes that clearly indicate that they are expecting food. Some crabs also show that they have a good memory of their home territory by their ability to return to their own burrow or crevice after foraging on the shore.

An instance of learning a new feeding habit was observed in the Plymouth Aquarium by Dr. D. P. Wilson. Four large spiny lobsters (*Palinurus vulgaris*) were kept in a tank with twenty or more hermit crabs which were carrying whelk shells. These two types of Crustacea lived together quite happily for several months, until, during a period when food was scarce, the spiny lobsters attacked the hermits, dragged them out of their whelk shells, and ate the soft abdomens. The spiny lobsters persisted in this habit even when provided with other food; eventually they had to be removed and replaced by others which had not acquired a taste for hermit crabs.

The new spiny lobsters lived peaceably with the hermits, even during periods of food scarcity. One wonders how the lobsters first found out about the abdomen of hermits. Did one find a hermit in the process of changing shells, or did it start by dragging a hermit out of its shell? Whichever way it started the others seem to have caught on to the idea and found the results to their liking.

LITERATURE

ALEXANDROWICZ, J. S. (1958). Further observations on proprioceptors in Crustacea and a hypothesis about their function. *J. mar. biol. Ass. U.K.* 37 : 379-396.

BURKE, W. (1954). An organ for proprioception and vibration sense in *Carcinus maenas. J. exp. Biol.* 31 : 127-138.

CLOUDSLEY-THOMPSON, J. L. (1952). Studies in diurnal rhythms. II. Changes in the physiological responses of the woodlouse *Oniscus asellus* to environmental stimuli. *J. exp. Biol.* 29 : 295-303.

CRANE, J. (1941). Crabs of the genus *Uca* from the West Coast of Central America. *Zoologica, N.Y.* 26 : 145-208.

DE BRUIN, G. H. P., & CRISP, D. J. (1957). The influence of pigment migration on the vision of higher Crustacea. *J. exp. Biol.* 34 : 447-463.

DIJGRAAF, S. (1956). Structure and function of the statocyst in crabs. *Experientia* 12 : 394-396.

FRAENKEL, G. S., & GUNN, D. L. (1940) *The orientation of animals.* Oxford.

HARRIS, J. E., & MASON, P. (1956). Vertical migration in eyeless *Daphnia. Proc. Roy. Soc.* B. 145 : 280-290.

PUMPHREY, R. J. (1950). Hearing. *Symp. Soc. Exp. Biol.* 4 : 3-18.

THORPE, W. H. (1956). *Learning and Instinct in Animals.* Cambridge.

WILSON, D. P. (1949). Notes from the Plymouth Aquarium. *J. mar. biol. Ass. U.K.* 28 : 345-351.

CHAPTER VII

ASSOCIATIONS WITH OTHER ANIMALS

As a crustacean makes it way around its environment it must inevitably encounter other animals; the results of these encounters can vary considerably. The two creatures may ignore each other, or, if the animal which is encountered is a predator the survival of the crustacean will depend upon its ability to escape or deter the assailant. If the crustacean is a carnivore and the meeting is with a potential prey species the roles will be reversed. But apart from these rather obvious possibilities there are many special relationships which may be entered into.

Of all the creatures with which the Crustacea come into contact, the coelenterates, which include the sea anemones, corals, jellyfish and their allies, seem the most prone to enter into special relationships. The crustacean may merely be a predator on a particular coelenterate, like the fresh-water cladoceran *Anchistropus* on *Hydra*, but there are other more complex relationships.

Hyperia galba is an amphipod which lives in the pits on the undersides of large jellyfish. It was once thought that no harm was done to the jellyfish, but recently it has been found that the amphipod actually eats some parts of its host. Several species of an allied genus, *Phronima*, live in the large spaces inside salps, which although they are not coelenterates resemble them in texture. *Phronima* has enormous eyes and peculiar modifications of some of the limbs (fig. 43); the body is very transparent, making it inconspicuous within the equally glassy body of the host. Most of the salps with *Phronima* inside are dead and so that it seems as if the amphipod is a predator which gets inside the salp and eats it.

The coral gall crabs (Family Hapalocarcinidae) live within the colonies of various corals, and produce galls by stimulating the colony to develop a chamber in which the female crab lives and communicates with the outside via a series of small holes. The crabs obtain their food by filtering small particles from the water which they cause to circulate in and out of the chamber. The male crabs are much smaller than the females and can enter the chamber

98

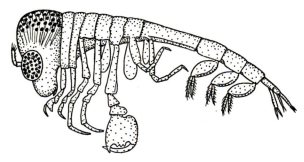

Fig. 43. *Phronima* sp. (Amphipoda) from inside a salp.
Actual length 13 mm.

through the small holes, for the purpose of mating and fertilising the eggs. A shrimp, *Paratypton siebenrocki*, has similar habits.

Sea anemones are rarely eaten by other animals, they appear to be distasteful, and they are well provided with stinging cells which are virulent enough to repel most would-be predators. Several crustaceans have taken advantage of these distasteful properties and gain protection by associating with the sea anemones. A recently described example is the mysidacean *Heteromysis actiniae*, which lives among the tentacles of the sea anemone *Bartholomea annulata* in the Bahamas. A more active use of a coelenterate for protection is made by the small crab *Lybia tessellata*, which carries a small sea anemone in each chela and thrusts them at its predators. It has been suggested that *Lybia* may also use the stinging powers of the anemones to disable small animals, which the crab then takes as its own food.

The associations between hermit crabs and sea anemones are classical examples of commensalism. This is a term applied to associations in which the two partners share the same food. Most hermit crabs hide their soft vulnerable abdomens in an empty mollusc shell. *Eupagurus bernhardus* is found most frequently in empty whelk (*Buccinum*) shells; this too is a special relationship. Even though the whelk is not a living partner the hermit depends upon its activities to produce the shell. A special case is found in Bermuda, where a land-dwelling hermit crab, *Coenobita diogenes*, lives in the shells of *Livona pica*. The remarkable fact is that *Livona* is now extinct in Bermuda, and all the shells used by the hermits are either fossils or sub-fossils; the crab relies on the products of a snail no longer in existence. One wonders how long this can go on, particularly as there does not seem to be any other suitable shell on the island.

The mollusc shells carried by the hermits provide the base for the attachment of sea anemones. The position occupied by the anemone may be variable, as in the association between *Eupagurus bernhardus* and the anemone *Calliactis parasitica*, or there may be a constant relation between the tentacular crown of the anemone and the mouth of the crab. *Eupagurus prideauxi* occupies shells too small completely to cover its abdomen, which is protected by the cloak-like base of the anemone *Adamsia palliata*. The mouth of the anemone is always positioned just behind that of the crab, so that any food caught by the crab is shared by the anemone. The association between the two species is obviously very close, and it has been found that the anemone produces toxins which are fatal when injected into other crabs, but which are neutralised by antibodies when injected into *Eupagurus prideauxi*.

Hermit crabs often have colonies of small hydroids, particularly of the genus *Hydractinia*, attached to the mollusc shells which they carry. These hydroids are also found attached to rocks and seaweeds, so that they are not obligatory commensals. A peculiar feature of the colonies carried by the hermits is that they have an additional type of zooid, a spiral one, the function of which is not really known, but it is thought to be protective. One species of *Hydractinia*, *H. epiconcha* from Japan, forms dense colonies which overlap the edges of the mollusc shell, and so provides protection for the hermit as it grows and relieves it of the task of finding a larger shell.

Hydroids are also sometimes found attached to parasitic copepods. Usually the hydroid concerned is a well-known, unmodified, free-living species, such as *Obelia geniculata*, which has been found on *Lernaeocera branchialis* (p. 113) attached to the gills of a cod (*Gadus*). A peculiar modified hydroid, *Ichthyocodium sarcotretis*, which lacks tentacles, has been found on a copepod, *Sarcotretes scopeli*, which attaches itself to the body of the small pelagic fish, *Scopelus glacialis*. It is not known how *Ichthyocodium* obtains its food.

Other creatures may join the hermit crab association. *Nereis fucata* is a polychaete worm which inhabits the whelk shells carried by *Eupagurus bernhardus*, and when the hermit captures some food the worm pokes its head quickly between the mouthparts of the crab and snatches a piece away. Another worm, *Lagisca extenuata*, is sometimes found in the large body whorl of the whelk shell, always with its head pointing towards the spire of the shell; the feeding habits of this worm are not known. Apart from these worms, some Crustacea may also join the assemblage. *Sunaristes paguri*, a copepod, is frequently present, and four species of amphipods have been recorded from shells carried by *Eupagurus*. In the Red Sea there is a mysid, *Gnathomysis gerlachei*, which is known only from the shells carried by the hermit, *Pagurus brevipes*. A peculiar cirripede, *Alcippe lampas* (fig. 44) burrows in the central column of whelk shells carried by hermits. This barnacle has reduced appendages, and dwarf males which lack a gut.

Sponges of the genus *Suberites* may also be found associated with hermit crabs and sometimes the sponge overlaps the mollusc shell and keeps pace with the growth of the hermit so that it does not have to seek a larger shell as it grows. This is a striking parallel with *Hydractinia epiconcha* described above.

Suberites also associates with dromiid crabs, which have hind legs bearing pincers. The crab takes small pieces of sponge in these

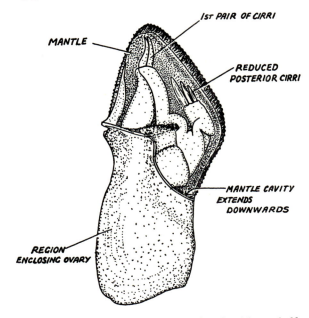

FIG. 44. *Alcippe lampas* (Cirripedia) female with one half of the mantle removed. Actual length 8 mm.

pincers and holds them on its back until they became fixed. The sponge grows and covers the back of the crab, giving it protection by virtue of its distastefulness to fish.

The echinoderms, which include the starfish, sea urchins and sea cucumbers, are another group with which the Crustacea frequently enter into special relationships. Often we do not know enough about the details of the relationship to be sure whether it is commensalism or parasitism. This is so in the case of *Micropontius ovoides*, a copepod which lives on the irregular urchin, *Spatangus purpureus*. The female of *Micropontius* is remarkable for producing only one large egg in each of her two ovisacs.

Frequently one finds that the associated crustacean and echino-derm are similarly coloured. Copepods of the genus *Ascomyzon* often match exactly the colour of the starfish on whose surface they live.

Sometimes the crustacean lives on a particular part of the echino-derm's surface. A crab, *Lissocarcinus orbicularis*, from Madagascar, lives near the mouth of a sea cucumber, and is sometimes actually enclosed within the tentacles of its host, but it comes to no harm. Another crab, *Eumedon convictor*, from the Gambier Islands, lives on the top of a sea urchin, *Echinothrix turca*, and causes the host's shell to fold back to form a sort of gall.

One of the simplest relationships with another animal is to live on its surface and to enjoy the benefits of free transport. Many barnacles attach themselves by chance to other animals, often on other large Crustacea, but some species regularly attach themselves to a particular type of animal. *Coronula* attaches to whales, *Stoma-tolepas* is found on turtles, and perhaps the most surprising, *Platylepas ophiophilus* has been found on the sea snake, *Enhydris curta*, in the Malay Archipelago.

A number of small creatures reverse the roles, and attach them-selves to various Crustacea.

An association between certain species of *Daphnia* and the rotifer *Brachionus rubens* has been analysed in a delightful manner by Viaud (1947). The rotifer (fig. 45) attaches itself to *Daphnia*, using its foot, and so gets transported by the water flea. Feeding currents are produced by the corona of the rotifer, and it obtains its food by selecting from the particles brought in by these currents. In this way the rotifer is independent of *Daphnia* for its food supply and so cannot be considered as a parasite. Moderate numbers of the rotifer do not appear to harm *Daphnia*, but large numbers, such as over 80 per individual *Daphnia*, hinder the movements of the water flea and interfere with its feeding. Viaud's analysis of the association showed that the rotifer is attracted to *Daphnia* by virtue of the characteristic swimming movements made by the water flea. An artificial water flea was made and was caused to move in water in various ways; the numbers of rotifers settling on the artificial host when it was moving in different ways was then recorded.

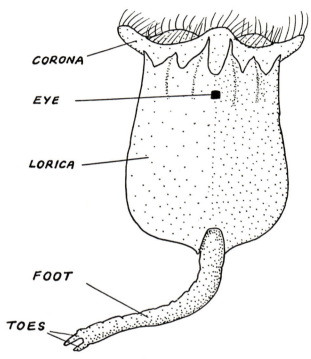

FIG. 45. *Brachionus rubens* (Rotifera) from the surface of *Daphnia obtusa*. The length of the lorica is about a quarter of a millimetre.

First the number of oscillations per minute was studied, and it was found that the greatest number of rotifers became attached when the artificial host oscillated at a rate of just over a hundred per minute. This is about the rate of the normal swimming movement of *Daphnia*. The amplitude, or height of the oscillation, was then studied, and again the greatest number of rotifers became attached when the amplitude was near to that of a normal free-swimming *Daphnia*. It is clear that the two components, frequency and amplitude, are appreciated by the rotifer, and it has evolved responses to them which lead to it attaching to any object moving in a manner similar to *Daphnia*. The association is not very specific as far as the species of *Daphnia* are concerned, but it is very specific with regard to the rotifer. There are other species of the genus *Brachionus*, some of which are difficult to distinguish from *B. rubens*, but most of them do not have the habit of attaching themselves to *Daphnia*. Two species which do have the habit are *B. variabilis*, which has been found on various daphnids in North America, and *B. sessilis* which attaches itself to another cladoceran, *Diaphanosoma brachyura*, in Europe.

Proales daphnicola is another rotifer associated with *Daphnia*. It is smaller than *Brachionus* and does not carry its own eggs, but sticks them on the surface of its host so that the emerging young do not have far to seek for a host.

Sometimes one finds that there is competition for space on the surface of a popular host. The epibionts, which are the organisms living on the surface, of *Daphnia*, show this rather well. *Colacium vesiculosum* is a relative of *Euglena*; it contains chloroplasts and so is capable of photosynthesis and independent existence, but it spends much of its life attached to *Daphnia*, and other small arthropods, by means of a gelatinous stalk. Peritrichs, such as *Vorticella* and *Epistylis,* also attach themselves to *Daphnia* by means of stalks, but they cannot photosynthesise; they feed on bacteria and other small organisms which they collect by means of ciliary currents. As a general rule it is found that when peritrichs are very abundant *Colacium* is scarce, and vice versa. Experiments show that the success or otherwise of *Colacium* can be influenced by light. If cultures of *Daphnia* which have been inoculated with swimming stages of peritrichs and *Colacium* are kept in the dark then *Colacium* fails to maintain itself in the face of competition from the peritrichs, which increase much more than they do in the light when they have to compete with a vigorous growth of *Colacium*.

An odd feature was found in a study of the distribution of *Colacium*, *Vorticella octava* and *Epistylis helenae* in small pools on the rocky islands off the south-west coast of Finland. When *Vorticella* was abundant the other two were absent, or sparse. This has been attributed to the fact that *Vorticella* has a contractile stalk, which must bring it frequently into collision with other epibionts and so render co-existence uncomfortable.

From living on the external surface to living on an internal surface is but a short step, which leads to parasitism. We cannot deal here with all the various parasites of Crustacea; the parasitic Crustacea are dealt with in the next chapter. Some Crustacea seem to be in the process of moving from the outside to the inside. Ostracods have been found in the gill chambers of fresh water crayfish in North America, and the copepod *Tisbe elongata* lives in the gill chamber of the lobster.

The water passages of sponges are often inhabited by a variety of small Crustacea, particularly shrimps of the family Alpheidae, and some stenopids, such as *Spongicola*, which lives in pairs inside the sponge known as Venus's Flower Basket. The shrimps enter the sponge when they are young, but cannot escape after they have grown. A pair of shrimps imprisoned in the skeleton of the sponge is sometimes given as a wedding present in Japan, to symbolise marriage until death.

One of the most interesting internal commensals is the copepod *Ascidicola rosea*, which lives in the oesophagus of ascidians or sea squirts. The host feeds by collecting small particles in mucus and making a food string which passes down the oesophagus under the influence of ciliary action. The copepod feeds on particles which it extracts from the food string. The legs bear long setae and the abdomen has a spiny pad for holding on to the string. As the string is continuously passing down the oesophagus the copepod has to climb upwards at intervals to maintain its position. After each climb it feeds for a while as it is transported downwards. The situation has a parallel in someone walking up a downward travelling escalator. The copepod does not spend all its life on the food string, but occasionally wanders down into the host's stomach and deposits some eggs which liberate nauplii, still enclosed in a thin membrane. These nauplii travel through the host's gut and escape from their membranes just as they are shot out with the exhalent stream of the water current that the host continually pumps through itself. The nauplii pass through six moults in six days and assume the form of copepodids which seek a new host.

Commensalism of a quite different type is found among certain woodlice. Some, such as *Kogmania* and *Schoblia*, live in galleries in termite nests, and others, such as *Platyarthrus*, live in ants' nests.

Platyarthrus hoffmannseggi can be found in the nests of many different species of ants, and it appears to be equally well tolerated by all of them. The woodlouse feeds on the faeces of the ants, and so helps to keep the nest clean, but it also supplements its diet with the sugary excrement of aphids which ants often keep in their nests. Pregnant females spread the species from nest to nest; they leave the nests at night and wander about; as daylight approaches they take cover again and are attracted towards ant nests by a positive reaction to the formic acid which ants produce.

This is a clear-cut example of a species responding to a particular chemical substance produced by the animals with which it associates. It is likely that many of the other more specific associations described above involve reactions to substances produced by the associates, but the substances are likely to be more complicated than the formic acid of ants.

LITERATURE

BORG, F. (1935). Zur Kenntnis der Cladoceran Gattung *Anchistropus. Zool. Bidr. Uppsala.* 15: 289-330.

CAULLERY, M. (1952). *Parasitism and Symbiosis.* London.

DALES, R.P. (1957). Commensalism. In: *Treatise on marine ecology and palaeoecology. Geol. Soc. Amer. Mem.* 67, Vol. 1. pp. 391-412.

GOTTO, R. V. (1957). The biology of a commensal copepod, *Ascidicola rosea* Thorell, in the ascidian *Corella parallelogramma* (Muller). *J. mar. biol. Ass. U.K.* 36: 281-290.

GREEN, J. (1957). Parasites and epibionts of Cladocera in rock pools of the Tvärminne Archipelago. *Arch. Soc. zool.-bot. fenn. Vanamo.* 12: 5-12.

MATHES, I., & STROUHAL, H. (1954). Zur Okologie und Biologie der Ameisenassel *Platyarthrus hoffmannseggii. Z. Morph. Okol. Tiere.* 43: 82-93.

VIAUD, G. (1947). Recherches experimentales sur les tropismes des rotifères. L'oscillorheotropisme de *Brachionus rubens* Ehrenberg, cause de la fixation de ce rotifère phoretique sur les daphnie et autre crustacés d'eau douce. *Ann. Sci. nat. Zool Fr.* (11) 9: 39-62.

CHAPTER VIII

PARASITIC CRUSTACEA

S o m e of the Crustacea mentioned in the last chapter approached a parasitic way of life. The borderline between the various associations described and true parasitism is overstepped when one of the associates begins to use the other as its food-source. True parasites are found mainly in three groups, the Copepoda, Cirripedia and the Isopoda. In each of these groups we find species with modifications of such a profound nature that without knowing the life history of the animal it would be quite impossible to identify it as a crustacean. Less profoundly modified parasites are found among the amphipods and the Branchiura. It will be convenient to deal with each of these groups separately.

PARASITIC COPEPODS

In the copepods one can find all stages from almost unmodified external parasites to internal parasites so modified that they can only be identified as copepods by their egg sacs and nauplius larvae. We can begin our account by tracing such a series; this must not be interpreted as a strict evolutionary sequence, because the examples have been chosen from widely divergent families.

Various members of the family Ascomyzontidae are found on echinoderms. These copepods have suctorial mouthparts and are assumed to feed on fluids which they extract from their hosts. Apart from this modification they do not differ very much in appearance from typical cyclopoids (fig. 46A).

Many species of the Caligoidea are parasitic on fish. The body differs in shape from that of a normal copepod, but there is no great difficulty in recognising the systematic position of a caligoid even when adult (fig. 46B). The abdomen is greatly reduced and various appendages on the head and thorax are modified for clinging to the skin or gills of the host. One member of the group, *Lepeophtheirus pectoralis*, attaches itself to the skin of the flounder, *Platichthys flesus*, and various other flatfish. It receives the name *pectoralis* because the mature females are usually found under the pectoral fins of the host. The eggs, which are compressed intc a cylindrical shape in the egg sacs, give rise to nauplii which sw_m freely in the plankton. The nauplii moult several times and then change into copepodids which seek out a fish and attach themselves to it. Attachment is effected by means of a thread made by a gland on the front of the head. Several moults are passed through in the attached copepodid, or chalimus, stage before the adult form is assumed. This type of life cycle is not very different from that cf a free-living copepod, and though *L. pectoralis* prefers flatfish i: is

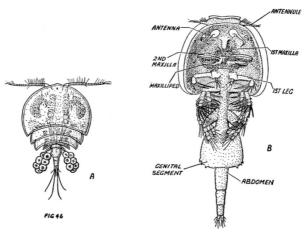

Fig. 46. Parasitic Copepoda. A, *Ascomyzon asterocheres*, from the common starfish, *Asterias rubens*. Dorsal view of female; actual length about 1·3 mm. (After G. O. Sars). B, *Trebius caudatus*, a common caligoid parasite of skates (*Raia* spp.) Ventral view, actual length about 8 mm.

not very particular about which sort of flatfish it attaches to. A closely related species, *L. pollachii*, is much more specific in its choice of habitat and is only found under the tongue of the pollack (*Gadus pollachius*).

Deviations from the typical copepod shape can occur in various ways. *Eudactylina* (fig. 47A), a parasite of sharks and rays, has become maggot-like, but it still has limbs which are quite typically copepodan. *Mytilicola intestinalis*, which lives in the gut of the common mussel (*Mytilus*), is even more maggot-like and the limbs are but poorly developed. The copepodan form becomes more obscured when lappets and projections are developed, as in *Lernanthropus* and *Chondracanthus* (fig. 47).

Another type of modification is the reduction of the body to a simple sac-like structure, while retaining a few appendages for attachment to the host.

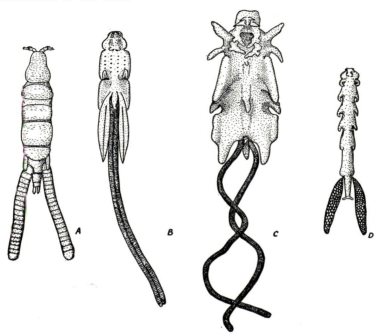

Fig. 47. Parasitic Copepoda. A, *Eudactylina rachelae*, dorsal view of a female from the gills of an electric ray (*Torpedo nobiliana*). Actual length of body, excluding egg sacs, 2.4 mm. B, *Lernanthropus kroyeri*, ventral view of a female from the gills of a bass (*Morone labrax*). Actual length, without egg strings, about 8 mm. C, *Chondracanthus lophii*, ventral view of female from the gills of angler fish (*Lophius piscatorius*). Actual length of body about 12 mm. D, *Mytilicola intestinalis*, ventral view of a female from the rectum of the common mussel (*Mytilus edulis*). Actual length excluding egg sacs, about 7 mm.

The Choniostomatidae are a family of copepods which parasitise other Crustacea, mainly Malacostraca, though one species, *Sphaeronellopsis littoralis*, is known to parasitise an ostracod. The adult females tend towards a spherical shape (fig. 48A), and the trunk limbs are minute, so that locomotion is impossible, apart from slight changes in position engineered by the maxillipeds. The males (figs. 48B, D) differ considerably in appearance from the females. Both males and females have a characteristic mouth cone which is expanded into a disc. The mandibles make a small hole in the body wall of the host, and blood is sucked out. Many of the species live in the brood pouches of their hosts and attach themselves to the oostegites. Egg sacs are produced by the females, and are usually freely disposed in the host's brood pouch. The fecundity of each female is remarkable; six or eight egg sacs, each the size of the female, may be produced. Free-swimming larvae hatch from the eggs. These larvae are of a typical copepodan appearance (fig. 48c), but they have the characteristic choniostomatid mouth cone. Some species (e.g. *Sphaeronella giardii*) go through a pupal stage; this forms from the larva when it finds a new host. It is from the pupa that the young males and females emerge. In some species (e.g. *Sphaeronella leuckarti*) only the females go through the pupal stage, and in others (e.g. *Aspidoecia normani*) the pupal stage appears to be missing; the young males and females develop directly from the larvae.

Rhizorhina ampeliscae is also a parasite on other Crustacea, in this instance on members of the amphipod genus *Ampelisca*. This is surprising, because *Rhizorhina* belongs to the family Herpyllobiidae, and all the other members of this family are parasites on polychaete worms. The adult female is spherical in shape and has no appendages at all, but she has a remarkable rooting process which branches within the body of the host. This in an interesting parallel with the Rhizocephala (p. 116), although the anatomical origins of the roots are very different in the two groups. The male of *Rhizorhina* is similar in appearance to the larvae of the Choniostomatidae, and is an example of precocious attainment of maturity while still in a larval form.

With the female *Rhizorhina* we have arrived at a stage equivalent to a sac feeding by means of roots. Can specialisation and simplification of structure go further? The answer is yes. *Xenocoeloma* is a parasite on a marine worm, *Polycirrus*. The adult of the copepod is merely a mass of tissue lying between the skin and the gut of its host; it has no appendages and has even lost its skin. Another remarkable fact is that it is hermaphrodite; this is a most unusual state for a copepod. The copepodan affinities of *Xenocoeloma* are revealed by its producing two long egg sacs, and by the nauplius larva which hatches from these eggs. Unfortunately we do not know the stages between the nauplius, which is normal apart from lacking a gut, and the adult.

Another aspect of the biology of parasitic copepods is seen when the life histories are compared, one with another.

Sometimes it is only the adult which is parasitic; *Thersitina gasterostei* spends its adult life attached to the gill cover of the stickleback (*Gasterosteus aculeatus*). The earlier stages in its life history are free living. In the caligoid life cycle, already described, attachment to the host occurs earlier, in the first copepodid stage.

A different type of life cycle is found in the family Monstrillidae. These hatch as nauplii, which lack a gut, and immediately seek a

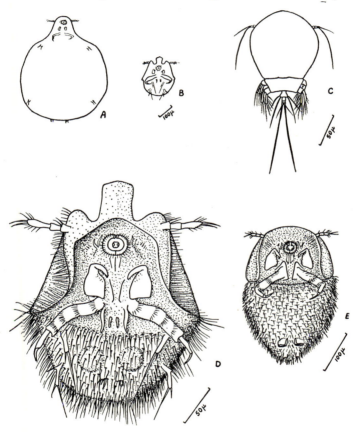

Fig. 48. *Sphaeronella danica* (Choniostomatidae), specimens from the brood pouch of the amphipod *Erichthonius brasiliensis*. A, female, ventral view. B, male, drawn to the same scale as A. C, larva, dorsal view. D, male, ventral view. E, a very young female, still retaining trunk hair and before the trunk has distended. Note the scales by each figure.

host. This is usually a worm or a mollusc. The nauplius breaks into
the body of the host, then loses its appendages and takes up
residence in a blood vessel. Two long processes then develop from
the surface of the parasite, and are thought to be concerned with
the absorption of food from the blood of the host. The body
gradually becomes longer, and an adult develops, which breaks out
of the host, leaving the cast larval skin behind together with its
long absorptive process. There is no digestive tube in the adult, so
that it cannot feed, it can however swim actively and forms the
main distributive phase of the life cycle. This is a marked contrast
with most parasitic Crustacea, which rely upon their larvae to dis-
tribute them while the adults are usually so grossly modified as
to be incapable of extensive locomotion.

The life histories of some species of *Lernaeocera* are remarkable
because two distinct hosts are involved. The adult female of
L. branchialis (fig. 49A) lives on cod, whiting and pollack (*Gadus*
spp.). Its body is large, swollen and deformed, with two long coiled
egg strings. The head is buried deeply in the tissues of the host and
penetrates the main artery leaving the heart, sometimes actually
entering the cavity of the heart. The copepod feeds on the host's
blood; it takes its meals infrequently, but digestion is complete, and
there is no anus for the expulsion of undigested material.

The eggs produced by the female *Lernaeocera* give rise to a
nauplius stage which lasts for about a day before it moults and
changes into a copepodid. The copepodid swims actively and
eventually attaches itself to the gills of a flounder (*Platichthys
flesus*). When the copepodid moults it produces an attachment
thread from a gland on the front of its head. This thread penetrates
the skin of the host and the attached larva is then known as a
chalimus. This is a modified copepodid stage which lacks swimming
setae on its legs. Four moults are passed in the chalimus stage then
the males become sexually mature and produce sperms which they
transfer to the females. Both males and females develop swimming
setae on their legs and can swim actively. The males die after
mating, but the females swim away in search of a member of the
cod family. When a cod is found the female enters its gill chamber
and attaches itself near the front of the fourth gill arch. Once
attached the female begins to grow. The body becomes longer and
bends into the characteristic shape of the mature female. The head
penetrates the tissues of the host and antler-like processes grow out
to act as anchors. Eventually all traces of appendages are lost and

the female resembles a fat worm. The whole cycle from egg to the death of the adult female takes about eight or ten weeks, and occurs throughout the year, so that there may be half a dozen overlapping generations in one year. The fish which are infected tend to linger for a greater length of time in shallow water than their uninfected fellows; this results in the nauplii being liberated in shallow water, where they are more likely to encounter flounders.

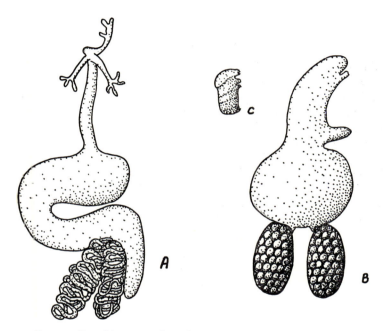

FIG. 49. Parasitic copepoda. A, *Lernaeocera branchialis*, adult female from the gills of whiting (*Gadus merlangus*). Actual length about 3 cm. B and C, *Brachiella obesa*, B, adult female, Oblique view, actual length, excluding egg sacs, about 3 mm. C, adult male, lateral view, drawn to same scale. Specimens taken from the gills of red gurnard (*Trigla cuculus*).

Lernaeocera branchialis is typically an inshore parasite. This is in contrast with a very closely allied species, *L. obtusa*, which has only very recently been recognised. The adult females of this species are found on offshore populations of the haddock (*Gadus aeglefinus*), and the chalimus stages are found on the lemon sole (*Microstomus kitt*). There is also a difference in the site of attachment of these two copepods: *L. branchialis* penetrates the junction of the heart

I

and the main artery, while *L. obtusa* restricts its point of attach-ment to the artery itself, sometimes not actually entering the main artery, but one of the branches to the gills. It has been suggested that the copepods find their way into the arteries by responding to the vibration produced by the beating of the fish's heart. It would follow from this that the two species have slightly different responses, *L. branchialis* tending to go nearer to the heart.

BRANCHIURA

All the members of this small order are parasites. The genus *Argulus* (fig. 50) is the best known, and is remarkable for the development of a large pair of adhesive suckers in place of the first maxillae. Most of the species are only about a quarter of an inch long, but *A. scutiformis* reaches a length of over an inch.

These creatures attach themselves to the skin of fishes; they have also been recorded on frog tadpoles, axolotls and the tadpoles of the smooth newt *Triturus vulgaris*. They are not permanent parasites, and may frequently be found swimming freely. The genus *Chonopeltis*, however, has lost the ability to swim and dies in a couple of days when removed from its host.

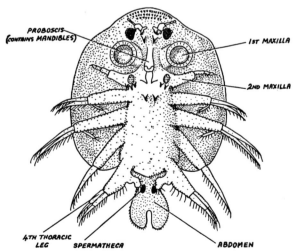

FIG. 50. *Argulus foliaceus* (Branchiura), adult female, found swimming freely in Regents Park Lake. Actual length about 5 mm.

The damage which branchiurans inflict on fish is probably not very serious in itself, but the small wounds readily become infected with fungi which may eventually kill the fish.

The eggs are laid in clusters attached to stones or other hard objects. There is considerable variation in the form of the youngster emerging from the egg. Sometimes it is not very different from the adult, but in other species it is more like a nauplius. The larva of *Chonopeltis inermis* hatches with an enormous pair of chelate first maxillae, which later become transformed into suckers. The life

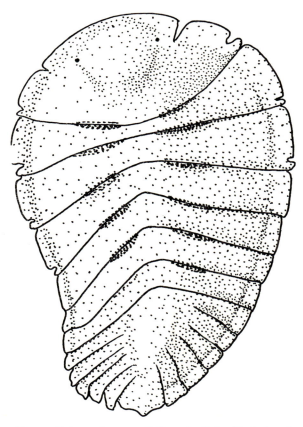

FIG. 51. *Bopyrus fougerouxi* (Isopoda, Epicaridea), dorsal view of adult female from the right hind gill chamber of *Palaemon* (=*Leander*) *serratus*. Note the asymmetry of the body, specimens from the opposite side of the host are bent in the opposite direction. Actual length about 8 mm.

history is quite straightforward, but the branchiurans differ frcm copepods in that they continue moulting when adult.

We have already seen (p. 102) how barnacles attach themselves to other animals and enjoy free transport. It is but a short step from this to becoming a true parasite. *Anelasma squalicola* seems to be in the process of taking this step. The lower part of the body is embedded in the skin of sharks, and gives off numerous root-like processes. The free outer part of the body bears appendages, but these are stumpy and lack the setae normally found on a barnacle. The creature has a mouth and an anus, so it presumably obtains some food from the water through which it is transported, but it also seems likely that it obtains food from the tissues of its host, via the rooting processes.

Another barnacle, *Rhizolepas annelidicola*, roots itself into a South African polychaete worm; it lacks a mouth and an anus, so that it must obtain all its food from the host. The part projecting from the host is similar in many respects to a normal stalked barnacle, but the mantle is reduced to a semi-cylindrical flap and does not completely enclose the body. The appendages are quite well developed, but there are no mouthparts.

Anelasma and *Rhizolepas* seem to have evolved from stalked barnacles by the simple development of rooting processes from the stalk. This is very different from the development of the rooting processes in the Rhizocephala. The name Rhizocephala means 'root head', and was given because it was thought that the rooting system was derived from the head. In fact the origin is very different, as the classical studies on the development of *Sacculina* have shown.

Sacculina is a genus with over eighty species, but one species, *S. carcini*, has been studied in great detail. This species is mainly a parasite on the common shore crab, *Carcinus maenas*, but it has been recorded on eight other species of the same family. The adult parasite appears as a sac on the under-surface of the crab, but its roots extend all through the host's body, even to the tips of its legs. Eggs, produced by the adults, give rise to nauplii which moult four times then change into cypris larvae in the usual barnacle fashion. The cypris finds a young crab, and attaches itself, by means of its antennules, to a seta, which may be located anywhere on the body of the crab. The larval limbs are cast off, leaving a small sac-like creature attached to the base of the seta. A hollow dart-like structure is developed; this penetrates the thin cuticle at the base of the crab's seta, and the contents of the sac are injected into the body of the crab. The small mass of undifferentiated cells migrates to a position below the crab's intestine and then starts putting out roots from a small central body. The roots spread throughout the host, and the small central body enlarges, eventually making a hole through the external skeleton of the crab and appearing on the outside in the adult form. The complete cycle takes about nine months.

A crab which is infected and carrying an adult *Sacculina* cannot moult, but nevertheless can continue living for at least a couple of years The reproductive organs of the crab are most seriously affected by the parasite. The testes and ovaries are rendered functionless, and the host usually dies without producing any offspring. Infected male crabs often lack their secondary sexual characteristics. This is particularly noticeable in the abdomen, which is usually narrow in the males and broad in the females; infected male crabs develop broad abdomens, and, in some species even develop the egg-carrying appendages characteristic of the females. All the changes observed in infected crabs have been towards feminisation. The females do not change their external appearance when infected.

Not all the Rhizocephala prevent their hosts from moulting. *Thompsonia*, which infects alpheid shrimps, produces numerous reproductive bodies all over the surface of its host, but these are cast off after they have produced a single brood of eggs, and the host can moult unhampered. *Thompsonia* is remarkable because a single rooting system gives rise to numerous external reproductive individuals, and successive generations of these are produced. The reproductive bodies have only got ovaries, and males are not known, so that parthenogenesis appears to be the rule. The whole structure and way of life of this parasite resembles that of a fungus; only the cypris larva gives a clue to its true identity.

Yet another group of the cirripedes, the Ascothoracica, have adopted a parasitic way of life, but their modifications are quite different from those of the Rhizocephala. The essential feature of the evolution of ascothoracicans has been progressive modification from a type similar to a cypris larva.

In *Laura*, which is a parasite on certain relatives of sea-anemones, the two valves of the carapace have become enormous relative to the size of the body, and are joined along the whole length of their edges apart from a small opening near the mouth. The parasite feeds by sucking fluid from the tissues of the host through a conical structure around the mouth. Branches of the gut and ovary ramify throughout the enlarged carapace. This branching of the internal organs is important, because it foreshadows the developments found in more highly modified members of the same group.

In *Myriocladus* and *Dendrogaster,* which are parasites of echinoderms, the outgrowths from the gut and ovary extend much further than the confines of the carapace, giving the animal a bush-like appearance. The small body lies at the centre of the ramifications, and houses the mouth, through which fluids are sucked from the host.

The males of all Ascothoracica are dwarfs and are to be found in the mantle cavity of the female; in general the males are much less modified than the females and are quite recognisable as modified cypris larvae.

It is a remarkable feature of parasitic Crustacea that no matter how bizarre and distorted the adult may be the larvae remain true to type. The persistence of a nauplius in *Sacculina* and of a cypris in *Thompsonia* illustrate this. A further point is that the males are often dwarfs, which retain larval characteristics. The cypris-like males of the Ascothoracica have just been referred to, and among the copepods the male of *Rhizorhina* is remarkably like the larvae of the Choniostomatidae. The precocious attainment of sexual maturity while still in a larval stage is a feature we shall meet again in the parasitic isopods, some of which provide a partial explanation of the phenomenon.

PARASITIC ISOPODS

All the members of one sub order of the isopods, the Epicaridea, are parasitic on other Crustacea. Their life histories are often complicated and involve two hosts. The eggs give rise to larval forms which are essentially typical little isopods, except that they have hooked claws on the legs, and the mouthparts form piercing stylets. This is known as the epicaridian stage, and it swims actively in the sea until it finds a copepod, such as *Calanus.* The epicaridium attaches to the copepod and sucks its blood. It remains on the copepod for six or seven days and passes through a couple of moults.

The body become longer and the larva is now called a cryptoniscus. This leaves the copepod and seeks out the final host.

In one family of the Epicaridea, the Bopyridae, the cryptoniscus makes its way into the gill chamber of a young decapod. The larva moults and loses the pleopods from its abdomen; it then grows in a series of moults, which coincide with those of its host. The parasite feeds by sucking blood, and this tempts one to think that the moults of the parasite may be influenced by the hormones circulating in the host.

The first cryptoniscus to take up residence in a gill chamber invariably develops into a female, and any later arrivals develop into males. As a rule only one adult male is found with a female. If a young female is removed from its host and placed in a gill chamber with a mature female, the development of the young one is retarded and it eventually becomes a male. Young males will develop into females if they are removed from the presence of a female and placed in a gill chamber of an uninfected crab.

The later development of the two sexes is rather different. The males remain small and resemble the cryptoniscus. The females grow considerably and sometimes lose some of their legs. The brood pouch develops on the underside and is often relatively enormous, capable of holding large numbers of eggs until they hatch as epicaridian larvae to start the whole cycle again.

Although the bopyrids are external parasites the draining of blood from the host has serious internal effects. In general these are similar to the effects of *Sacculina* on crabs. The reproductive organs of the host are reduced, and parasitised males become feminised. These effects are so marked that some of the early biologists thought that only female hosts were infected.

The Liriopsidae, which form another family of the Epicaridea, are parasites on the Rhizocephala; they are parasites of parasites. *Danalia* is a parasite on *Sacculina*, and *Liriopsis* parasitises *Peltogaster*, which is itself a parasite on hermit crabs. It is interesting that *Liriopsis* has a similar effect on *Peltogaster* to the effect which *Peltogaster* has on its host. The ovaries of an infected *Peltogaster* are usually degenerate and poorly developed. However, the isopod does not live as long as its cirripede host and it eventually drops off. The ovary of *Peltogaster* then regenerates, and eggs are produced.

Distortion of the grossest kind is found in members of the family Entoniscidae (fig. 52). These are internal parasites of crabs. In life they are enclosed in a membrane which is made by the crab. In the later stages of infection the cavity enclosed by the membrane communicates with the outside via a hole in the inner wall of the host's gill chamber. The usual epicardian larval stages are passed through, and the parasite enters the crab as a cryptoniscus. This moults and loses its limbs so that it resembles a small maggot. The blood cells of the host react to the presence of the parasite by gathering around it and enclosing it in a membrane, but the young parasite makes a hole in this membrane so that it can obtain food from the host's blood. The male is very much smaller than the

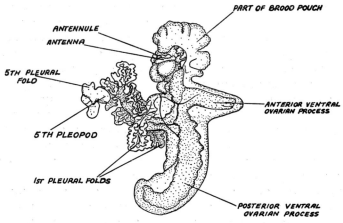

FIG. 52. *Pinnotherion vermiforme* (Isopoda, Epicaridea, Family Entoniscidae). Young adult female from body cavity of a pea crab (*Pinnotheres pisum*). Actual length about 13 mm. (After Atkins, 1933).

female and spends its life in her brood pouch. As in the other epicarideans the male is quite recognisable as an isopod.

All the parasitic isopods we have dealt with so far have been parasitic on Crustacea. There are others which parasitise fish. The Gnathiidae are the most interesting of these because they are only parasitic in the young stages and are free-living as adults. The adults are found in small groups, usually one male with several females, in crevices in rocks, or in tunnels in the banks of estuaries. Different species inhabit different localities: *Gnathia oxyuraea* is found on rocky shores, and *Paragnathia formica* in estuaries; yet other species, such as *Bathygnathia curvirostris*, are only found in the abyssal depths of the sea.

The larval form of the gnathiids is quite a normal looking little isopod, but its mouthparts are modified for piercing and sucking the blood of fish. One such larva, *Praniza milloti*, has been found attached to the coelacanth, *Latimeria*. After the larva has gorged itself the third, fourth and fifth thoracic segments are distended to about twice the diameter of the rest of the body. The larvae probably remain parasitic for several months, after which they leave their hosts and take up residence in adult quarters. The adult male has a very large head and mandibles, but the other mouthparts are reduced and do not function. Neither male nor female feed in the adult state. The females are less modified than the

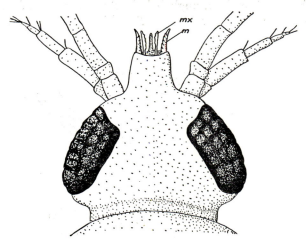

FIG. 53. Head of a larva of *Paragnathia formica* (Isopoda, Family Gnathiidae). Only the bases of the antennae are shown. m = mandible. mx = maxilla.

males; they brood their eggs in internal sacs, and die when their larvae have been released.

The Gnathiidae are quite a separate group from the Epicaridea, and they do not help in trying to trace the evolution of the latter group. More help is given by members of the family Cymothoidae. These are also parasitic on fish, but only as adults. In some cymothoids the females are somewhat asymmetrical when mature, recalling the asymmetry found in the Bopyridae. Another interesting feature is that the males often develop into females later in life, showing that the sex is not very strongly determined, and indicating how the lability of the sex in the Bopyrids may have arisen.

PARASITIC AMPHIPODS

It only takes a glance at a whale louse to realise that it is adapted to clinging. The limbs are strongly hooked, and the body is flattened. Unfortunately very little is known of the biology of these creatures. There are five genera, and of these four have only one species each. The number in the main genus, *Cyamus*, is uncertain, but not high. The various species have been found on and in the skins of whales from various parts of the world.

Apart from the whale lice there is a notable lack of parasites among the amphipods, though it is likely that some of the forms with modified mouthparts, such as *Trischizostoma*, are parasites on fish.

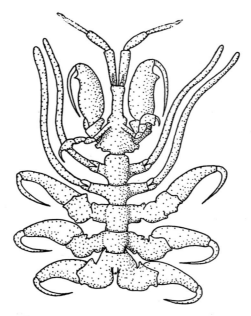

FIG. 54. *Cyamus boopis* (Amphipoda).
Ventral view of a specimen from a
humpback whale (*Megaptera nodosa*).
Actual length about 12 mm.

LITERATURE

ATKINS, D. (1933). *Pinnotherion vermiforme* Giard and Bonnier, an entoniscid infecting *Pinnotheres pisum. Proc. zool. Soc. Lond.* 1933: 319-363.

BAER, J. (1951). *Ecology of animal parasites.* Illinois.

DAY, J. H. (1939). A new cirripede parasite, *Rhizolepas annelidicola* nov. gen. et sp. *Proc. Linn. Soc. London (zool.)* 151: 64-79.

FRYER, G. (1956). A report on the parasitic Copepoda and Branchiura of the fishes of Lake Nyasa. *Proc. zool. Soc. Lond.* 127: 293-344.

GREEN, J. (1958). Copepoda parasitic on British Amphipoda (Crustacea), with a description of a new species of *Sphaeronella. Proc. zool. Soc. Lond.* 131: 301-313.

HARDING, J. P. (1950). On some species of *Lernaea* (Crustacea, Copepoda: parasites on fresh water fish). *Bull. Brit. Mus. (Nat. Hist.) Zool.,* 1 (1): 1-27.

KABATA, Z. (1957). *Lernaeocera obtusa* n.sp., a hitherto undescribed parasite of the Haddock (*Gadus aeglefinus* L.). *J. mar. biol. Ass. U.K.* 36: 569-592.

MONOD, T. (1926). Les Gnathiidae. Essai monographique. *Mem. Soc. Sci. nat. Maroc.* No. 13, pp. 668.

SCOTT, T., & SCOTT, A. (1913). *The British Parasitic Copepoda,* Vol. 1, 252 pp.; Vol 2, Plates. London, Ray Society.

SMITH, G. (1906). Rhizocephala. *Fauna et Flora Neapl.,* vol. 29, pp. 122.

CHAPTER IX

DISTRIBUTION

I t is already evident from the preceding chapters that Crustacea
are found in the sea, in freshwater, and on land. In dealing with
their distribution in more detail it is necessary to discover how the
various groups have distributed themselves within these major
habitats, and to try to explain how various factors combine to
limit or facilitate distribution.

Numerous references will be made to endemic species; these are
species which are peculiar to a particular region, and are not found
elsewhere. Such species, and, more particularly, endemic genera,
are most important in attempting to define zoogeographical
regions.

MARINE CRUSTACEA

Most Crustacea live in the sea, and in all parts of the world they
form a major component of the marine fauna. This world-wide
distribution raises certain questions. Do the crustacean faunas of
the various oceans differ one from another? Do the inland seas,
such as the Caspian, have different Crustacea from those seas which
are in open communication with the great oceans, and if such
differences are found can we account for them?

Animals living in the sea can be roughly divided into those
which spend most of their time on the bottom, and those which
swim or float freely in the water. The latter are more likely to be
widely distributed, because they may come under the influence of
the oceanic currents. Differences between the faunas of geographical
areas of the seas are more likely to be found among the bottom
dwellers.

The sea floor can be divided into two parts: the shelf, which sur-
rounds most land masses to a varying degree, extending down to
a depth between 200 and 400 metres, and the deep sea floor which
falls away steeply from the shelf and reaches depths of several
thousand metres. Depths below a thousand metres are referred to as

the abyss. The sea floor between the shelf and the abyss contains the bathyal or archibenthic fauna, which is to some extent an intermediate type, but often contains species characteristic of deeper waters.

The Crustacea of the deep sea floor sometimes belong to primitive groups. The decapod family Eryonidae, such as *Stereomastis* and *Polycheles*, are otherwise known only as fossils, dating back to the Jurassic rocks, which were laid down over a hundred million years ago. In fact the fossils were known before deep-sea exploration revealed the presence of living members of the family. The modern eryonids are all blind, but some of the fossils had well-developed eyes, and lived in shallower water. The persistence of primitive

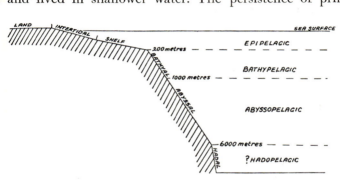

FIG. 55. Diagram of the main zones in the Sea. The various depths are not drawn to scale. The question mark in front of hadopelagic is necessary because pelagic animals are not yet known from the hadal regions.

groups in deep water is probably due to the unchanging character of the ocean floor over vast periods of time.

Reduction of the eyes is frequent among the truly deep-water species, but in the upper archibenthal zone, where a little light may still penetrate, or where phosphorescence may provide sufficient illumination for limited vision, the eyes are sometimes enlarged. It has even been suggested that one large-eyed hermit crab, *Parapagurus pilosimanus*, finds it way about by the light emitted by the phosphorescent sea anemones which it carries as a cloak over its abdomen.

An anatomical peculiarity which is often found in various bottom dwellers of the deep sea is an enormous elongation of the legs and antennae. Two examples are given in figs. 56 and 57. Long legs might be useful for walking across the ooze which covers so much of the ocean floor. The long setae on the front legs of *Platymaia* may be used as a rake for separating edible material from the ooze, and the fantastic chela of *Thaumastocheles* might also be used for a similar purpose.

Another peculiarity of the deep-water Crustacea is that they are often larger than their close relatives from shallower water. The most striking example of this is the isopod *Bathynomus giganteus*, which reaches a length of ten inches; among other isopods a length of three inches is exceptional. Among the Tanaidacea too the deep water forms are the largest. *Neotanais giganteus* and *Herpotanais kirkegaardi* reach lengths of 20 and 25 millimetres respectively. A length of 10 millimetres among the tanaids from shallower water is exceptional enough to elicit admiration.

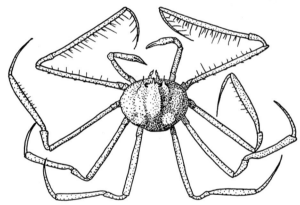

Fig. 56. *Platymaia alcocki* (Brachyura). A bottom dwelling spider crab from the depths of the Indian Ocean. Actual width of carapace about 9 cm. (After Doflein).

Relatively large eggs are also of frequent occurrence among the deep-sea Crustacea. Large eggs are usually associated with the elimination of early larval stages so that the young hatch at an advanced stage of development. It is not known why this should be advantageous in the deep sea, but it may well be due to a shortage of food suitable for larvae.

A special name is given to the deepest parts of the oceans; depths greater than 6,000 metres are known as the hadal region (from Hades, the mythical ruler of the Greek underworld). Such regions occur as faults or trenches in the sea floor. The Crustacea of this region are not well known, but it is possible to say that the isopods, amphipods and Tanaidacea are quite well represented. The isopods in particular seem to have a number of species confined to this region; *Macrostylis galatheae* is the deepest recorded species, being found at a depth of 9,790 metres in the Philippine Trench. The only crustacean known from deeper water is an unidentified amphipod from 10,190 metres.[1] Decapods have not been found in the hadal region, but some ostracods, a barnacle, mysids and a cumacean have been dredged up from the various trenches of the Pacific.

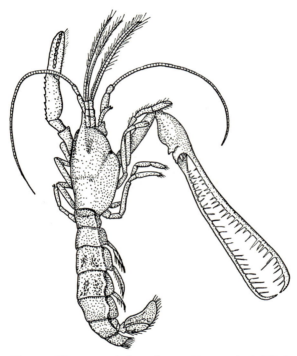

FIG. 57. *Thaumastocheles zaleucus* (Astacura). A blind deep sea decapod, from a depth of over 800 metres off the West Indies. Actual length of body about 10 cm. (After Spence-Bate).

Too little is known about the distribution of the deep-water Crustacea to make any definite assertions. It seems probable that most of the abyssal genera are cosmopolitan where the oceans are deep enough, but the species are more restricted in their distribu-

[1] Since this account was written both amphipods and isopods have been recorded from 10,687 metres in the Tonga Trench.

tion. If the distribution of the hadal isopods is studied it is found
that most of the genera occur in all the oceans, but only five per
cent of the species are found in more than one ocean. It is likely
of course that the hadal species will be less widely distributed than
ordinary abyssal species because the hadal zone occurs in the form
of trenches which are to a large extent isolated from each other,
and only form 1·2 per cent of the area of the oceans. It is worth
noting that the abyssal zone is by far the most extensive habitat in
the world; 76 per cent of the area of the oceans and over half the
surface of the whole globe is occupied by the abyssal depths of the
sea.

There is great uniformity in the conditions on the abyssal floor.
The temperature is low, between 2 and 4° C., and the salinity is
practically constant everywhere. The main variable is pressure,
which increases directly with depth, so that in the hadal zone it
may be five times as great as at the beginning of the abyss. The
uniformity of temperature and salinity offers a partial explanation
of the cosmopolitan distribution of many abyssal forms; once a
creature has become adapted to such conditions there will be no
great barrier to its spreading.

The only abyssal area which has been studied in sufficient detail
for its bottom dwelling fauna to be characterised is the Norwegian
Basin, lying between Norway and Greenland. The endemic Crustacea of this region include the isopod *Mesidotea megalura*, which
is a close relative of the glacial relict *M. entomon* which we will
meet in the Caspian and the Baltic. Others, such as the amphipod
Bruzelia dentata, and the mysid *Pseudomysis abyssi*, may also be
regarded as characteristic of this area.

The animals of the shelf are more distinctly divided into
geographical units than those of the deep sea. The various faunas
have been dealt with most admirably by Ekman (1953), who con-
siders all types of animals, not just the Crustacea. Ekman's main
divisions of the shelf fauna have been adopted in the account which
follows.

There is a vast circumtropical area, with a great wealth of species,
lying between the water isotherms for 20° C. at the coldest part of
the year. A diluted version of this fauna extends to the regions with
a minimum water temperature of 16-18° C. Two very characteristic
associations are found on this warm-water shelf: coral reefs and
mangrove swamps, each with its own type of crustacean fauna.

PLATE III

Serolis bromleyana (Isopoda)

The genus *Serolis* has numerous species, all in or near Antarctica. This is a specimen from Chatham Rise, collected by the New Zealand Chatham Island Expedition.

PLATE IV

Blepharipoda occidentalis
A sand crab which burrows backwards using the
modified legs. Actual length about three inches.

In the coral reefs the crab family Xanthidae is particularly well represented; *Carpilius maculatus* is a widespread example of this family, being found in South Africa, throughout the Indian Ocean and over a large part of the Pacific. This crab is buff or orange in colour, with eleven large blood-red spots on the carapace. In the Barrier Reef of Australia it is called the Barometer Crab because of a local belief that the spots alter in density with the weather (see p. 60 for the possible truth of this). Some of the Crustacea become intimately associated with the corals and live in galls which they cause the corals to form (see p. 98).

Mangrove swamps provide shelter for a great variety of mud-burrowing crabs and shrimps. Related species often inhabit different parts of the swamp: *Sesarma taeniolata* is found higher up the shore than *S. bataviana* in the mangroves of the East Indies. Other crabs of the genus *Uca*, are often very abundant among the roots of mangrove trees; and burrowing shrimps, such as *Thalassina* and *Callianassa* are sometimes present in large numbers so that the whole surface of the mud is pitted with their burrows.

The warm-water shelf has three major divisions: Indo-West Pacific, East Pacific, and Atlantic. Oddly enough the last two have more in common than the first two. The vast expanse of deep water in the Pacific has been an effective barrier between the two shelves to the east and west. Some shelf Crustacea are circumtropical and are found in all three areas. One such crab is *Grapsus grapsus*, but it is not really a typical example of a shelf animal because it often clings to floating weeds and turtles and so becomes widely distributed.

Quite a high percentage of the larger Crustacea are very widely distributed in the Indo-West Pacific region: thirty per cent of the crabs found in the Red Sea are also known from Hawaii. *Lupa pelagica* is a typical example of a widespread Indo-Pacific species, ranging from the east coast of Africa to Japan and New Zealand, and is one of the species that has migrated from the Red Sea through the Suez Canal into the Mediterranean.

The similarity between the warm-water shelves of the two sides of the Americas can be illustrated by reference to certain crab genera. About 18 per cent of all the crab genera of America are found on both sides of the continent. *Mithrax*, for instance, has 21 species on the Atlantic side and 11 on the Pacific side. The two sides have however been separated long enough for most of the species to be different. Often one can find species pairs, which are closely allied species of the same genus occurring on opposite sides

K

of the continent; the spiny lobsters, *Panulirus interruptus* on the Pacific side, and *P. argus* on the Atlantic side, make a good example.

The Pacific and Atlantic shelves of America also have their own characteristic crab genera. *Lophoxanthus* and *Pliosoma* occur only on the Pacific Coast, while the genera *Carpoporus* and *Lupella* are found only on the Atlantic Coast.

The warm-water Atlantic shelf of Africa is singularly poor in endemic genera of Crustacea; having only the crab *Atlantotlos* with a single species, but the number of endemic species is high. About 40 per cent of the West African decapod Crustacea are not found elsewhere. An odd feature of the West African shelf fauna is the presence of a number of genera which are otherwise characteristic of the Indo-West Pacific. These genera, such as the crabs *Thalamita*, *Heteropanope* and *Notopus*, are thought to have entered the area when there was a sea connecting the Indian Ocean with the Mediterranean Sea, which also had a much wider connection with the Atlantic than it has at present.

The shelf faunas of the Arctic and Antarctic seas form a marked contrast with the warm-water shelf fauna. There are many fewer species, but a high proportion are endemic. In the Antarctic there are some 310 species of Amphipoda, and about 70 per cent of these are not found elsewhere. The isopod genus *Antarcturus* has about fourteen species, ten of which are restricted to the Antarctic. The Arctic also has its endemic species; the shrimp *Sclerocrangon ferox*, and eight of the eleven species of the amphipod genus *Onisimus*, are confined to this region.

Between the warm-water and polar shelves are the temperate water shelves. These too have characteristic Crustacea, such as *Crangon allmani* from the European shelf, and *Oregonia gracilis* which spans the temperate Pacific from California to Japan. The stomatopod, *Squilla armata*, provides an example of a widespread southern temperate shelf species; it is found on the coasts of Chile, Cape Horn, South Africa, New Zealand and South-West Australia.

One surprising feature of the crustacean fauna of the North Atlantic shelf is that a large part of it is derived from the Pacific, and it can in some ways be regarded as a poorer version of the North Pacific fauna. For instance, the genus *Spirontocaris* has 64 species in the two oceans; 51 of these are purely N. Pacific, 10 are common to the N. Pacific and N. Atlantic, and only 3 are purely N. Atlantic. Another example is given by the edible crab, *Cancer*, which has only three species in the N. Atlantic while the N.

Pacific has eight species of the genus. These facts, together with information about the fossils in the two areas, indicate that the waters of the N. Pacific have been temperate for a longer period than those of the N. Atlantic. When, during the Eocene, Britain had a tropical climate the warm water in the N. Atlantic reached further North than did the warm water in the Pacific, so that a temperate water fauna developed first in the N. Pacific, and only later in the N. Atlantic.

Separate faunas are more difficult to distinguish when we leave the sea floor and examine the swimming and floating Crustacea. These are usually sub-divided according to the depth at which they are found. The Crustacea swimming in the upper 200 metres are part of the epipelagic fauna in contrast to the bathypelagic and abyssopelagic fauna swimming below this depth.

Some of the epipelagic copepods are cosmopolitan; *Oithona similis* is found from the Arctic Sea, through the Mediterranean and Red Seas, and over the Indian and Pacific Oceans to the Antarctic Seas. Some live all round the globe, but are confined to the colder waters, or descend into the deeper cooler water in tropical regions. It is thus possible for a species to be epipelagic in temperate waters and bathypelagic nearer the equator.

The only geographical division of the epipelagic Crustacea that can reasonably be made at present is into a warm-water fauna and a northern and a southern cold-water fauna. There are many examples of circumglobal warm-water species, perhaps the most interesting is the mysidacean *Siriella thompsoni*, for most other Mysidacea live only in the waters above the shelves. The Northern cold-water epipelagic forms can be typified by the copepod *Pareucheta glacialis*, while in Antarctic waters the Euphausiacea are important, particularly *Euphausia superba*, which forms the main food of the whalebone whales in this area.

As one passes downwards in the sea, through the epipelagic and into the bathypelagic zone, there is a change in the species of Crustacea which one finds. Particular species swim at their own specific depths. The prawn *Systellaspis debilis* swims between 150 and 500 metres from the surface, while *Hymenodora glacialis* swims between 700 and 1,200 metres. Both these depths are the day-time depths, for, like most other planktonic animals, these Crustacea migrate upwards during the night. A further instance of variation in the specific composition of the crustacean fauna with depth is found when the numbers of species of copepods at various depths are compared. In the Indian Ocean about 109 species live near the surface, only 9 species are found at 300 metres below the surface, but the number increases to 24 at about 1,000 metres then decreases again to 2 at 2,000 metres.

Like their relatives on the deep-sea floor, the bathypelagic Crustacea are often larger than their shallow-water relatives. The ostracod *Gigantocypris* deserves its name, for it is the size of a cherry, while most other members of the Ostracoda are but a couple of millimetres long. Among the amphipods, *Cystisoma* reaches a length of two inches or more while most others in the group are less than half this length.

Various bathypelagic Crustacea are limited in their distribution, but it has not proved possible to define any clear-cut faunistic regions. The nearest approach to a geographically defined bathypelagic fauna is in the Arctic Sea, including the Norwegian Basin. The most characteristic species of this region is the amphipod *Cyclocaris guilelmi*. This species, and two other rarer amphipods, are the only crustaceans in this rather limited fauna which do not occur elsewhere. Some others of the bathypelagic Crustacea are very widespread; *Sergestes arcticus*, which lives at a depth of 400-800 metres during the day, may be regarded as cosmopolitan, and the large primitive mysidacean *Gnathophausia gigas* is found in all the oceans.

CRUSTACEA OF THE INLAND SEAS

The inland seas gradually develop more characteristic faunas the greater their isolation from the oceans. The Crustacea of the Mediterranean are not markedly different from those in the Atlantic outside the Straits of Gibraltar; in fact, nearly 60 per cent of the Norwegian species are found in the Mediterranean. Nevertheless it can be said that there is a faunistic unit which includes the Mediterranean and the western Atlantic from Capo Blanco to the western entrance to the English Channel. A number of Mediterranean Crustacea extend around the north-western coast of Africa, and have their northern limits on the south-western coasts of Britain. The large spider crab, *Maia squinado*, will serve as an example. The opening of the Suez Canal contributed an eastern element to the Mediterranean Crustacea. Some of the crabs from the Red Sea, such as *Myra fugnax* and *Lupa* (=*Neptunus*) *pelagica* have been found on the north-eastern shores of Cyprus.

The Black Sea communicates with the Mediterranean through the Bosphorus and the Sea of Marmara, but the number of species of Crustacea is greatly depleted when compared with the Mediterranean. There are, for instance, only four species of barnacles, compared with more than 40 in the Mediterranean, and 35 decapods compared with over 200 Mediterranean species. But the Black Sea Crustacea are not to be thought of as merely as a diminished selection of Mediterranean species, even though this is largely true. There is another element in the fauna, known as the Sarmatian relict fauna, which dates from the time when a great inland sea extended from the Caspian to the Black Sea and even into Greece and Jugoslavia. This relict fauna is sometimes called the Caspian element of the Black Sea Fauna. Comparison of the Crustacea from these two seas, together with the Sea of Azov, shows that they have about thirty species in common, which are not found elsewhere. An interesting feature is that most of these species inhabit estuaries in the Black Sea, but live in the open waters of the Caspian. This may be explained by the fact that the average salinity of the Caspian is only two-thirds of that of the Black Sea. Further, the salinity of the Black Sea is only one-half of that of the Mediterranean. This provides an explanation of the impoverishment of the Black Sea fauna when compared with the Mediterranean; the reduced salinity acts as a barrier to the immigration of the more strictly marine Crustacea.

The Caspian is even more isolated than the Black Sea, and has a higher proportion of endemic species. The most striking example of endemism is found among the Cumacea; the family Pseudocumacidae has radiated into nineteen distinct Caspian species. Apart from ancient endemic groups there are also a few Crustacea which appear to have come from the Arctic Sea. *Mesidotea entomon* is a large isopod otherwise found in the Arctic and Baltic Seas, while the amphipod genus *Pseudalibrotus*, with two species in the Caspian, is found in the Arctic Sea, but not in the Baltic. It is thought that at one time a great ice-lake connected the Baltic and the Caspian, and possibly another such lake connected the Caspian with the Arctic in the region of the Kara Sea. These lakes would provide the Arctic fauna with a means of access to the Caspian.

Recently there have been additions to the Caspian Crustacea which are due to man's activities. Two species of the prawn *Leander* were deliberately introduced in the early 1930's, and the barnacle

Balanus improvisus appears to have been transported accidentally by vessels from the Sea of Azov through the Volga-Don Canal. This latter species has increased rapidly in what has been described by a Russian biologist as a 'biological explosion'. *Balanus eburneus* is the most recent species found in the Caspian, but no explanation of its occurrence has yet been offered.

The Aral Sea has a very poor selection of Crustacea, with no crabs, only one amphipod (*Pontogammarus aralensis*) and under thirty of the smaller Crustacea. The numbers of each species are also low compared with other areas. The ostracod *Cyprideis littoralis* is found in hundreds of thousands per square metre in the Sea of Azov, but barely a thousand per square metre are found in the Aral Sea.

The Baltic differs from the other inland seas in that it is further North and, on the average, has less salt dissolved in it. The communication between the Atlantic and the Baltic is by means of the Skagerrak and Kattegat, then through the narrow channels between the Danish Islands. There is a considerable difference between the salinities of the waters on the two sides of the Danish Islands. In the middle of the Kattegat the salinity is about two-thirds that of the North Sea, while at the southern tip of Sweden there is only half this concentration of salts. The salinity decreases as one passes up the gulfs of Bothnia and Finland. Many Crustacea of the Kattegat do not enter the Baltic; 64 species of decapods are known from the Kattegat, only thirteen from south of the Danish Islands, and but two from the gulfs of Bothnia and Finland. Different species of the same genus penetrate the Baltic to different extents; of the barnacles, *Balanus crenatus* get as far as the South of Denmark, while *B. improvisus* gets well into the gulfs of Finland and Bothnia.

The reduced salinity of the Baltic is not the only factor which limits the spread of Crustacea. *Rhithropanopeus harrisi tridentatus*, a small crab, was introduced into Europe before the end of the eighteenth century and lived mainly in the brackish waters of Holland. From there it was transported by Dutch boats to the Kiel Canal and has since entered the Baltic north-west of Kiel, but it does not seem to be spreading any further. Salinity is not the limiting factor, because this species can live in fresh water, it seems that the low temperature of the Baltic in winter is too severe to allow any further spread.

Apart from the marine animals which have penetrated from the

Atlantic there are several genuine brackish water Crustacea living in the Baltic. These are also found living in brackish water in other parts of Europe, and are frequent in the middle reaches of estuaries. The amphipods are the best represented, with such species as *Bathyporeia pilosa*, *Gammarus zaddachi*, *G. duebeni* and *Melita palmata*.

Migration into the Baltic from fresh water has also occurred. This has been enabled by the great stability of the salinity over wide areas. Many fresh-water Crustacea can become adapted to a certain amount of salt in the water provided it does not fluctuate very much. The common fresh-water isopod, *Asellus aquaticus*, seems to have made the greatest progress in this direction, and may be taken in dredges from the sea bottom at the entrance to the Gulf of Finland.

The final, and in many ways the most interesting, component of the Baltic fauna is made up of glacial relicts. Most of the glacial relict Crustacea are also found in the Arctic Sea, and seem to have entered the Baltic from an ice lake which was formed near the White Sea and which must have communicated with the Gulf of Finland after the last glaciation. Some of these relicts, such as the isopod *Mesidotea entomon*, and the amphipod *Pontoporeia affinis*, have since become isolated in certain fresh-water lakes around the Baltic. This isolation has been brought about by the gradual elevation of the land (which is still proceeding in some parts of the Gulf of Bothnia at a rate of three feet in a century) cutting off basins which gradually freshened due to the inflow from rivers.

SALINITY AND THE DISTRIBUTION OF CRUSTACEA

The importance of the salinity of the medium as a factor in the distribution of Crustacea has already been mentioned, but it is worthwhile examining the effects of dissolved salts in more detail. As mentioned earlier (p. 39), the amount of salt in the blood of a marine crustacean is similar to that in sea water. When the amount of salt in the surrounding water is reduced, as in estuaries, the animal will be subjected to osmotic stress—water will tend to flow into the blood, and the animal will swell, unless it can prevent the entry of water, or has an efficient means of removing it. If for instance the crab *Maia squinado* is placed in 80 per cent sea water its weight increases rapidly. About three hours later the weight is reduced to its normal level, and it is found that the concentration of salts in the blood is similar to that in the medium around the crab. It is found that whatever the concentration of the medium may be the blood of *Maia* become adjusted to the same concentration, which proves fatal if it is much different from sea water. A crab such as *Maia* is termed a non-regulator; it cannot control the concentration of its blood when subjected to osmotic stress. It follows that such Crustacea must necessarily be restricted to living in the sea. *However*

Estuarine Crustacea often exhibit considerable powers of regulating the concentration of salts in their blood. The common shore crab, *Carcinus maenas*, can keep its blood at a concentration well above that of the diluted sea water in which it often lives. Surprisingly it cannot keep its blood concentration down if kept in external concentrations higher than sea water, and further it cannot live in really fresh water. There is another crab, *Eriocheir sinensis*, which can do both these things; it is a better regulator. The concentration of its blood can be kept below that of a medium stronger than sea water, and the crab penetrates hundreds of miles inland up rivers. However, the adult *Eriocheir* must return to the sea to breed, and the breeding females are not capable of living in fresh water.

How can one species of crab withstand large changes in the concentration of its medium, while another cannot? The complete answer is not known. but there are various indications of the mechanisms involved. The outer covering of the regulators is much less permeable than that of the non-regulators, and various species can be arranged in a series according to their permeability. Such a series coincides remarkably well with the dilution of the external medium that can be withstood by the various species. The following results from Nagel (1934) illustrate this. The permeability of the cuticle was estimated by measuring the concentration of iodine in the blood after the crabs had been immersed for $2\frac{1}{2}$ hours in a solution containing sodium iodide.

TABLE 3

Concentration of iodine in the blood, as per cent of that in external medium.

Portunus	98
Carcinus maenas	12
Potamobius (fresh-water crayfish)	3
Eriocheir sinensis	0·0

The table shows that the non-regulator *Portunus* had allowed the concentration of iodine in the blood to become almost equal with that in the medium, while in *Eriocheir* the amount which penetrated was too small to be measured.

The crabs which regulate their internal concentration are known to be able to take up salts from media which are more dilute than the blood. This seems to be done mainly through through the gills. If the gills of *Eriocheir* are removed from the body they will still actively take up salts from dilute media. The active nature of this uptake of salts by the gills has been demonstrated by the fact that it stops in the absence of oxygen, and is inhibited by various substances which interfere with the chemical processes involved in respiration.

Another method of controlling the concentration of the blood is to regulate the flow of urine from the excretory organ. The antennal gland of *Carcinus* produces more urine when the crab is in half-strength sea water than when it is in undiluted sea water. This crab copes with the tendency for the blood to become diluted by increasing its output of urine to get rid of excess water, and, like *Eriocheir*, it takes in salt through its gills. Surprisingly it has been found that *Eriocheir* produces the same amount of urine in both sea water and fresh water. The low permeability of *Eriocheir*, combined with its ability to take in salts from dilute solutions, seems to have made unnecessary any increase in urine production in fresh water.

TABLE 4

Rate of urine flow in certain decapod Crustacea.

Species	Medium	Rate of flow (ml/day per 50 gm. body-wt.)
Carcinus maenas	Sea water	5·0
„ „	Half sea water	8·5
Eriocheir sinesis	Sea water and fresh water	3·0
Potamobius (fresh-water crayfish)	Fresh water	2·0
Palaemonetes varians	Sea water	4·8
„ „	5-10% sea water	19·5
Palaemonetes antennarius	Fresh water	20–26

Table 4 gives the rate of urine production in several different Crustacea. The fresh-water crayfish also seem to have adapted themselves so that they do not have to produce a great flow of urine. The most interesting feature of the table is the great production of urine by the fresh-water prawn *Palaemonetes antennarius*, which, in relation to its size, produces ten times as much urine as a crayfish. It seems that *P. antennarius* has comparatively recently entered fresh water and has not yet adjusted its rate of urine production. The table also shows that the rate of urine production is about that which might be predicted from its brackish water relative *P. varians* if it were to live in fresh water.

Fresh-water Crustacea make some concessions to their environment in that they do not maintain the concentration of their blood as high as that of their marine relatives. A reduction in the concentration of the blood is a convenient method of reducing the osmotic stress, for the gradient between inside and outside will not be so great and so will be easier to maintain. The concentration of salts in the blood of the European crayfish is just under half that of sea water, and it maintains this concentration in river water with less than one-hundredth the concentration of the sea.

There is evidence from the structure of the crayfish antennal gland that this organ can reabsorb salts from the urine. The fresh-water crayfish has an extra loop in the gland, which is not present in its marine relatives. Fresh-water amphipods also have larger excretory organs than the marine members of the same order. But this is not a general rule; the fresh-water crabs have antennal glands which are similar in size and structure to those of their marine relatives. That the extra loop in the crayfish antennal gland functions in reabsorbing salts has been shown by measuring the concentration of chlorides at the beginning and end of the loop. At the end of the loop, nearest the opening to the outside, the concentration is less than half the concentration at the beginning.

Large fresh-water Crustacea, such as crabs and crayfish, deal with the problem of osmotic stress in three ways. They are only slightly permeable, they take in salts through their gills, and they reabsorb salts from their urine. The smaller Crustacea are not so easy to study, and much less is known about their methods of regulating the concentration of their blood. Many of them are very permeable to water. Experiments with *Daphnia magna* show that there is 80 per cent exchange between the blood and surrounding water in about two minutes. Nevertheless *Daphnia magna* can live for about ten days without food in pure distilled water, and can live a normal life in very dilute solutions. There must be a very efficient mechanism for retaining salts and for taking them into the blood from dilute media.

Most fresh-water Crustacea have become so completely adapted to their medium that they cannot tolerate sea water. *Daphnia pulex* dies in less than twenty hours in water containing one part in six of sea water, and dies correspondingly quicker in higher concentrations. A notable exception to the general rule is the fresh-water race of the large isopod *Mesidotea entomon* from lakes in Sweden. This species also lives in the Baltic and Arctic seas. The specimens from the Baltic cannot be acclimatised to live in fresh water, but the specimens from the fresh-water lakes can be acclimatised to live in full-strength sea water. This is taken as a sign that *Mesidotea* is a recent immigrant into fresh water, and in fact the fresh-water lakes in which it lives came into being after the Ice Age (see p. 135).

So far we have been dealing with the problems which arise when a crustacean lives in water which is more dilute than sea water, but there are some inland waters which contain more salt than the sea. Few Crustacea can live in such places, and by far the most successful of these is the brine shrimp, *Artemia salina*. This anostracan can survive in water so saturated with salts that crystals form around the edge of the pool. It can also survive in water that is only one-tenth the strength of sea water. However, in nature it is not usually found in water less than twice the strength of sea water. Clearly such an animal must have an efficient means of regulating the composition of its blood. Recent studies by Croghan (1958) have shown that *Artemia* can keep the concentration of salt in its blood well below that of the strong brines in which it swims. When in water which is eight times as strong as sea water *Artemia* keeps its blood only slightly more concentrated than sea water. The gills play an important part in this process by excreting salt, while the gut is also important in actively taking in water to compensate for that which tends to be lost by osmosis to the strong outside medium. Salt is also taken in through the gut, and a balance is established between the intake through the gut and the output through the gills.

It is clear from the last paragraph that *Artemia* could live in the sea, or even in more dilute water. Its absence from such situations is to be explained by its vulnerability to attack by predators; it is an easy prey for small fish and large water beetles. The lower limits of salinity in which *Artemia* may be found may be said to correspond roughly with the upper limits of salinity tolerance of its predators. Salinity only limits the distribution of *Artemia* in the sense that a high salinity is necessary to eliminate its predators.

Inland saline waters often have a chemical composition rather different from that of the sea. In some cases this allows fresh-water Crustacea to live in higher concentrations than they could if the dissolved salts were the same as those in the sea. The importance of the chemical nature of the dissolved salts can be illustrated by reference to *Daphnia magna*. In natural waters this species has been found living in concentrations up to about a third that of sea water, while pure sodium chloride solutions with one-seventh the concentration of the sea rapidly kill it.

It is evident that as well as the amount of salt, its chemical composition is also an important factor in the distribution of Crustacea. But we cannot make any general statements about the effects of various salts in natural habitats because we do not yet know enough about the subject.

FRESH-WATER CRUSTACEA

The geographical units of fresh water are much more clearly defined than the subdivisions of the sea, and there are correspondingly clearer faunistic divisions. The ancient lakes provide excellent examples of distinct and characteristic faunas. Lake Baikal has been the scene of almost riotous evolution among the gammarid amphipods; about three hundred species are found in the lake, and only one of these, the common *Gammarus pulex*, is found elsewhere. The rest of the world has just about as many gammarid species as Lake Baikal. An interesting species flock has also appeared in Lake Nyasa, though the numbers involved are not so fantastic. The copepod genus *Lernaea* is parasitic on fish, and there are about thirty species known in the world; eight of these species are found in Lake Nyasa, and of these seven have not been found elsewhere. Lake Tanganyika has been the site of evolution of a species flock of *Argulus*, also parasitic on fish, and to some extent replacing parasitic copepods, which appear to be rare in this lake.

When dealing with the marine Crustacea it was not feasible even to mention all the various groups, because practically all the groups are well represented in the sea. Fewer groups have successfully penetrated into fresh water and so may be dealt with more systematically.

The Notostraca, Anostraca and Conchostraca, sometimes known collectively as the phyllopods, have a world-wide distribution, though within each group there is often a division into distinct geographical units. Longhurst's study of the Notostraca has shown that in the genus *Triops* (fig. 5) the four species occupy different parts of the globe, with only two of them overlapping. *Triops granarius* is the most widespread member of the genus, being found from South Africa across Asia to China; *Triops cancriformis* is found from North Africa and Western Europe to Russia and India; *T. longicaudatus* is an American species extending across the Pacific to Hawaii, Japan and New Caledonia, and *T. australiensis* is found in Australia and Madagascar. These species seem to have divided the world fairly evenly between them. The peculiar distribution of *T. australiensis* is a feature which will be echoed when the distribution of fresh-water crayfish is described.

It is characteristic of most phyllopods that they are inhabitants of temporary pools, usually in arid climates. They cannot withstand competition from the insects and more highly evolved Crustacea which are present in permanent pools. The few species of phyllopods which are found in permanent pools usually appear for a short time in the spring, grow very rapidly, and produce resting eggs before the other inhabitants of the pools have become properly active after their winter inactivity.

The Cladocera have but a few genera, such as *Podon, Penilia* and *Evadne*, in the sea, but in fresh water they are among the most abundant and prolific of all Crustacea. Various species occupy different parts of the environment. Some, such as *Holopedium* and *Leptodora*, are purely planktonic, others associate with weeds, yet others such as *Macrothrix* and *Camptocercus* skim over the bottoms of pools, and some, such as *Ilyocryptus*, burrow in mud and have lost the power to swim. The systematics of the group are difficult, because the form of the body often changes with the seasons, and from place to place. Because of these systematic difficulties it is hard to get a clear geographical picture of the distribution of Cladocera. All that can be safely said is that there appears to be a cosmopolitan group of species, with *Chydorus sphaericus* as their most ubiquitous member, a pan-tropical group, including such species as *Macrothrix triserialis*, and *Ilyocryptus spinifer*, and apart from this there are various species which are so far known to have limited distributions.

Within the genus *Daphnia* there has been an interesting radiation to produce lake plankton forms from different groups of the genus in various parts of the world. In Europe the lake plankton species belong mainly to the *D. longispina* group. In North America the *D. pulex* group has also produced a crop of lake dwellers, while in Africa and Australasia the sub-genus *Ctenodaphnia* is responsible.

Ostracods and copepods are also abundant in fresh water, but it is difficult to make any general statement about their zoogeography. The best example of a distinct fauna within these groups is found in Lake Tanganyika. The ostracods are here represented mainly by two genera with 11 and 8 endemic species respectively, while among the copepod genera *Shizopera* has produced eight endemic species, *Eucyclops* is represented by 7 species, 4 of which are endemic, and *Microcyclops* adds another 6 endemic species.

Although many copepods and ostracods are widespread, certain areas of the earth can be characterised by endemic fresh-water genera of these two groups. The copepods *Orthocyclops* and *Pentacamptus* are characteristic of North America; *Afrocyclops*, *Afrocamptus*, and the ostracod *Afrocypris* are endemic in Africa—examples could be multiplied. The point is not to produce lists for various localities, but to show that the ostracods and copepods are by no means as cosmopolitan as was at one time thought.

Few members of the Malacostraca have penetrated into fresh waters, but their distribution is better known because they are generally more conspicuous. But first there are a few inconspicuous members of this group. The Spelaeogriphacea are known from a single species, *Spelaeogriphus lepidops*, described in 1957 from caves in South Africa. The Thermosbaenacea also have a couple of cavernicolous species, *Monodella argentarii* and *M. stygicolla*, both from Italy. Another member of this order, *Thermosbaena mirabilis*, lives in warm water springs in Tunisia. The temperature tolerated by this small creature is remarkably high, about 47° C. *Thermosbaena* is remarkable in that it cannot tolerate even moderately lowered temperature; it becomes moribund at 35° C., which is a temperature high enough to kill most ordinary fresh-water crustaceans. A few other Crustacea can tolerate warm water, the ostracod *Cypris balnearia* being the most notable example. This creature can live in water at 51° C. and disappears in places where the temperature falls below 40° C.

The genus *Bathynella* was first found in a deep well near Prague in 1882, and was not found again until 1914, when it was discovered in a well-boring near Basel. Since then various species of the Bathynellacea have been found in Africa, Malaya, Japan and from the mouth of the Amazon. It is probable that when more caves are explored the various small Malacostraca will be found to be widespread. Recent evidence for this view is the discovery of *Rhopalonurus holthuisi*, a small peracaridan of uncertain affinities, which was found in a cave in the West Indies.

The Anaspidacea are larger relatives of the Bathynellacea; at the present time they are confined to fresh waters in Tasmania and the district around Melbourne in Australia, but in the past they were more widespread, as evidenced by fossils from the Carboniferous deposits of North America and Europe.

The large number of species of the amphipod family Gammaridae in Lake Baikal has already been mentioned; other species of the family are common in fresh waters in various parts of the world. Another family, the Talitridae, has produced a small flock, belonging to the genus *Hyalella*, in the fresh waters of South America. Apart from these two families (which also have many marine representatives) there are only occasional species from other amphipod families which have taken to living in fresh water. *Corophium curvispinum* is an example; this species lives in various rivers in Europe, and in the northern parts of the Black and Caspian Seas. It seems most probable that it migrated into the rivers from these dilute seas.

Isopods are best represented in fresh waters of the Northern Hemisphere by members of the Asellidae, and less well by occasional species from other families. The most important of these families are the Sphaeromidae and the Cirolanidae. About a dozen species of the former family, belonging to the genera *Monolistra, Microlistra* and *Caecosphaeroma*, are known from fresh water in caves of Europe. It is perhaps significant that the genus *Sphaeroma* is particularly abundant in brackish water.

A few parasitic isopods are known from fresh water, for instance, *Probopygrus bithynis* is found as a parasite of the fresh-water shrimp *Macrobrachium* in Central America.

The Phreatoicidea are a peculiar group of isopods (fig. 58), which at first sight look remarkably like amphipods; they are found in the fresh waters of Australia, New Zealand and South Africa, and may be thought of as the counterpart of the Asellidae in these areas.

Tanaidaceans do not seem to have taken to fresh water very well,

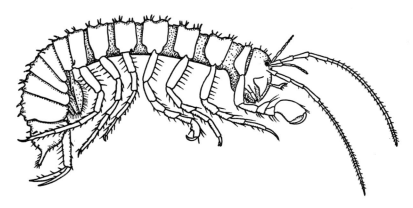

FIG. 58. *Phreatoicus tasmaniae* (Isopoda). A fresh-water form which superficially resembles an amphipod. Actual length of body about 2 cm.

only a few non-marine species are known, such as *Tanais fluviatilis* from the Argentine and *T. stanfordi* in the Kurile Islands.

The best known of the fresh-water mysids is undoubtedly *Mysis relicta*, which is found in various lakes in North America and Europe. *Mysis oculata* is a close relative which lives in the Arctic Ocean. It is thought that *M. relicta* has evolved from *M. oculata* after being isolated in lakes formed during the Ice Ages. The Arctic origin of the species is confirmed by its preference for cold lakes and its winter breeding habits. *Mysis relicta* starts laying eggs when the temperature falls below 7° C. and stops again when the temperature rises above this level.

Other mysids are known from fresh waters in caves; *Troglomysis vjetrenicensis* from Herzegovinia, and *Spelaeomysis bottazzii* from Italy, though the water in which the latter species was found was slightly brackish.

There are no fresh-water Euphausiacea, but the Decapoda are quite well represented in fresh water and their distribution is comparatively well known. Crayfish can be arranged in two families, the Potamobiidae in the Northern Hemisphere and the Parastacidae in the Southern Hemisphere. Both families live mainly in the temperate regions so that there is a vast area of the tropics which lacks crayfish; they are also absent from the whole of Africa, but present in Madagascar.

Various genera of crayfish characterise different parts of the world. Among the Parastacidae, *Astacopsis* and *Engaeus* are found in Australia and Tasmania; the latter island claims the distinction of having the world's largest crayfish, *Astacopsis franklinii*, which reaches a weight of eight or nine pounds. *Parastacus* is found in South America, while Madagascar has the genus *Astacoides*.

In North America the Potamobiidae are represented by *Potamobius* (= *Astacus*) to the west of the Rocky Mountains, while the sub-family Cambarinae, which includes *Troglocambarus*, *Orconectes* and other genera as well as *Cambarus*, is found only to the east of these mountains. The European species belong to the genus *Potamobius*, but a species of *Cambarus* has been introduced into Germany. There are no crayfish in the greater part of Asia, but the genus *Cambaroides* is found in Korea and the northern islands of Japan. Some authorities believe that *Cambaroides* is allied to *Cambarus*; if this is so the distribution of the northern crayfish is extremely puzzling because it means that two parts of the sub-family Cambarinae are isolated by *Potamobius*, which occupies the west of the North American continent.

A most striking feature of the distribution of fresh-water decapods is that it is only in the regions where crayfish are absent that other groups have become established in large numbers.

The two most important families of fresh-water shrimps are the Palaemonidae and the Atyidae. The latter are small, but some palaemonids reach a length of about a foot. Both families occur throughout the tropics, but a remarkable flock of atyids has arisen in Lake Tanganyika; eleven endemic species are found. This is in great contrast with the other African lakes, such as Nyasa and Victoria, each of which have only a single, non-endemic, species of prawn.

Only one anomuran genus is known from fresh water, this is *Aegla*, which looks like *Galathea*, and has about twenty species living in streams in southern Brazil and Chile.

Two families of crabs have representatives in fresh water: the Grapsidae and the Potamonidae. The latter are the true river crabs, spending all their lives in fresh water. This is also done by some of the grapsids, but many of them, like *Eriocheir sinensis*, have to return to the sea to breed (see p. 136). Both families are well represented throughout the tropics, and one true river crab, *Telphusa fluviatilis*, is found in countries on the northern shores of the Mediterranean.

L

CRUSTACEA ON LAND

Life on land presents difficulties which are not encountered when living in water. Temperatures are liable to fluctuate more violently, and there is the ever-present danger of drying-up, which can rapidly prove fatal. A crustacean living on land must be capable of resisting such adversities. Many crustaceans do this by means of their behavioural responses, which tend to keep them in cool moist places (p. 94). They also have some physiological adaptations which enable them to conserve water and to delay death from desiccation.

First there are those Crustacea which can be regarded as amphibious; they spend some of their time in water and some on land. The isopod *Ligia oceanica* is a good example of this group; it wanders about on the seashore, and sometimes strays inland for a short way. The concentration of salts in its blood shows comparatively large variations; it seems as if *Ligia* has developed a tolerance to such variation, which enables it to withstand a certain amount of drying, hence concentration of the blood, without ill effect. This ability to allow a certain amount of evaporation to occur is probably useful when the animal is exposed to the hot sun, because evaporation of water cools the surface from which it is evaporating. In this way *Ligia* can keep its temperature a few degrees below that of its surroundings, which may make all the difference between survival and death when temperatures are high.

Some crayfishes habitually leave the water and make burrows in soft earth. In these burrows they keep cool and moist, and so are not exposed to the more extreme conditions of life above ground. This is similar to the way in which many semi-aquatic species survive on the seashore; they make burrows in sand or mud, or hide beneath seaweed and stones. In this way they are protected from the heat of the sun until the tide returns to cover them.

The land crabs are the most conspicuous of the terrestrial Crustacea, and of these the Robber Crab, *Birgus latro*, is probably the best known. This is a large crab, weighing up to 5 or 6 pounds, which is widespread in the Indo-West-Pacific areas. It spends most of its time on land, even climbing up trees, but the females return to the sea to release their young, which hatch in the zoea stage and spend the early part of their lives floating in the sea. In common with other land crabs the gills of this species are small, but the gill chamber is modified for aerial respiration by having spongy walls which are richly supplied with blood vessels. The problem of desiccation is met by this tropical species in three ways; the shell is relatively impermeable so that water loss is reduced, the creature can tolerate some increase in the concentration of its blood without ill effect, and the Robber Crab is a good regulator, so that when it finds a pool of water it can soon restore its blood to a normal level. Strangely enough it is possible to drown this crab if it is forced to be immersed for a day or so; this is probably due to the fact that it is an air-breather and cannot obtain sufficient oxygen from that dissolved in water.

Representatives of the smaller Crustacea are also found on land, notably among the damp leaves of forest floors. Several harpacticid copepods are known from such situations, and recently an ostracod, *Mesocypris terrestris*, has been discovered among forest humus from South Africa. The only apparent modification which this ostracod shows is a strengthening of the limbs for moving about among the humus.

A few amphipods also live on the floors of forests. One of these, *Talitroides alluaudi*, has been introduced into greenhouses in various parts of Europe along with tropical plants, and is now established and breeding in these artificial conditions as far north as Helsinki.

The most numerous Crustacea dwelling entirely on land are the Oniscoidea or woodlice. These isopods live in a variety of habitats, mostly in places that are somewhat damp. The different genera and species differ in their abilities to survive in dry air, but all of them have to return to damp air fairly quickly to avoid death from desiccation. One wonders why they have not developed a water-proof covering of the type found in the insects. The answer to this may be that a permeable cuticle allows cooling by the evaporation of water, as we have already seen in *Ligia* (p. 146), which is a member of this group. The advantages of this cooling effect at critical temperatures may have been sufficient to prevent water-proofing from becoming established.

The Oniscoidea are not very different in structure from other isopods. The only obvious structural modification to terrestrial life is that some of the more advanced members have small tubes called pseudotracheae in their pleopods. These increase the respiratory efficiency of the pleopods in air, by taking air nearer to the tissues, but they do not penetrate beyond the pleopods and so cannot approach the efficiency of the tracheae in insects, which ramify throughout the body.

The isopods were in a sense pre-adapted for life on land. They have biting mouthparts for feeding on large particles; any crustacean with a filter mechanism obviously could not leave the water and still be able to feed. The possession of a brood pouch in which the young develop until they are liberated as miniature adults is also an important pre-adaptation. A crustacean with a nauplius, or any other type of swimming larva, could not forsake the water without at least the necessity of returning to liberate its young. A further pre-adaptation is found in the structure of the legs, which are well suited for walking on land.

When the woodlice moved from water to land they encountered a completely new type of predator—the spider. The importance of spiders as predators of small land-dwelling creatures should not be underestimated. It has been calculated that there is an average of about 50,000 spiders per acre over the whole of England and Wales. As a protection against this horde of predators the woodlice have developed a series of glands along the edges of the body which discharge a distasteful fluid when the woodlouse is bitten by a spider. This might seem a bit late in the day to start repelling one's assailant, particularly when it has a poisonous bite, but it has been found that woodlice can withstand a single spider-bite without apparent ill effect. The spider, after it has bitten a woodlouse, shows obvious signs of distaste and wipes its mouthparts vigorously.

The success of woodlice as land animals is due to the combination of the pre-adaptations described above, the development of distastefulness to a particularly important group of predators, and their behavioural responses (chapter 6) which keep them in damp places and so protect them from the danger of desiccation.

DISTRIBUTION OF ALLIED SPECIES

Within the various groups of Crustacea there is a tendency for allied species to live in similar places. The ostracods of Germany provide a good example. Most of them can be ranged in two families: the Cypridae and the Cytheridae. There are twenty German genera of the Cypridae; of these, only two have representatives in brackish water, and all the others are confined to fresh water. This is in marked contrast to the Cytheridae, which have twenty-three genera in the sea and only three genera in German fresh waters.

When the distribution of such a group is analysed in detail it is found that although there is a general resemblance in habitat even very closely related species show small but distinct differences in their preferences. A good example of closely related species with a distinct and measurable difference in habitat is found in the isopod genus *Tylos*. The species now known as *T. sardous* and *T. europaeus* were at one time regarded as a single species, but there are some small distinctive anatomical features which enable the two to be separated. Both species live on sandy shores of the Mediterranean, but *T. sardous* lives on coarser beaches than *T. europaeus*. Samples of sand from beaches on which these isopods live have been analysed by passing the sand through sieves of various sizes, and then determining the percentage by weight of each size of grain. All the beaches with *T. europaeus* had 90 per cent of their particles with a diameter less than half a millimetre, while the beaches with *T. sardous* had 65-90 per cent of their particles with a diameter greater than half a millimetre. Further, three out of four beaches with *T. sardous* had 20-30 per cent of their particles with diameters greater than five millimetres, which gives the beaches a gravel-like character. The difference is so striking that the expert can predict which species he will find merely by passing the sand through his fingers.

Less striking, but nevertheless quite recognisable differences can be found in other groups. One of the most outstanding studies on the systematics and distribution of related species has been the unravelling of the species of *Gammarus* living in British estuaries. Perhaps the most important step in this process was the recognition that the species known as *Gammarus marinus* is in fact an assemblage of half a dozen species having sufficient differences from other *Gammarus* to be included in a separate genus, *Marinogammarus*. We shall only consider the remaining species here.

As one passes inland from the mouth of a typical English estuary the species of *Gammarus* are encountered in the following order: *G. locusta*, *G. zaddachi salinus*, *G. zaddachi zaddachi*, *G. duebeni*, and *G. pulex*. The last species is confined to fresh water, while *G. duebeni* is found in fresh water on the western side of Britain, mostly in places where *G. pulex* does not occur. From a study of the distribution of these two species it has been deduced that *G. pulex* is a later arrival than *G. duebeni*; but when it becomes established it is more successful than the latter species and replaces it, so that *G. duebeni* is restricted to brackish water in estuaries which have *G. pulex* at the fresh-water end.

Gammarus duebeni also meets competition towards the seaward end of an estuary, where it is replaced by *G. zaddachi*. This latter species occurs in two forms which occupy different parts of the estuary: *zaddachi* is very hairy and lives in more dilute water than *salinus*, which is less hairy. There is a third form: *G. zaddachi oceanicus*, which is even less hairy and is more marine than the other two forms, but rather surprisingly it penetrates into quite dilute water in the Gulf of Finland.

The succession of species along an estuary has been confirmed several times and appears to be quite constant. We do not yet know how the sequence is maintained, but it is probably due to competition between the various species which are all very similar in structure and general habits. The way in which competition acts is not known; it is certainly not due to fighting or active damaging of one species by the other.

Competition can also be invoked to explain the distribution of some fresh-water species of *Gammarus*. We have already seen how *G. pulex* appears to have replaced *G. duebeni* in fresh water except on the western side of Britain. It also seems likely that *G. pulex* can replace another species, *G. lacustris*, which is thought to have survived the last glaciation, whereas *G. pulex* has invaded since the last glaciation. These two species do however tend to occupy slightly different habitats; *G. pulex* prefers cleaner, less silty, water than *G. lacustris*.

Yet another species, *G. fasciatus* (= *tigrinus*), has been introduced into Britain from North America, and seems to have made its own niche in somewhat salty waters that *G. pulex* cannot live in; it is also found in really fresh water in Northern Ireland where *G. pulex* has not penetrated.

The important feature which emerges from a study of this type is that the detailed distribution of allied species in a given area is determined in an interdependent manner. The range of a species is often limited by the ranges of its allies.

MIGRATION AND DISPERSAL

It has already been hinted that the distribution of Crustacea is not a static affair. Many planktonic forms migrate up and down in response to alterations in light intensity, and many get caught up in the great ocean currents. These two examples serve to differentiate two main ways in which dispersal can be achieved: it may be due to the animals own locomotory activity, or it may be passive so that the animals own locomotory efforts are not directly involved.

The most spectacular of the migrations performed by the Crustacea is the annual march to the sea by land crabs of the family Gecarcinidae. The common West Indian species, *Gecarcinus ruricola*, comes down from the hills in swarms during the rainy season in May. The crabs spend a couple of weeks on the beaches and the females enter the sea to allow the young to hatch from the eggs. When this has been done the crabs migrate back up to the hills until next year. They are followed a few weeks later by the young crabs which have passed through their larval stages in the sea.

Marine crabs and shrimps show comparable migrations due to their own locomotory activities. Many species move offshore during the winter and return to shallower water during the spring and summer. Marking experiments with crabs and lobsters have revealed that although these creatures indulge in their offshore migrations they do not migrate very far away from their own particular patch of coast. The really big migrations are those made passively under the influence of the oceanic currents.

Some species are distributed as adults by the ocean currents. Crabs of the genus *Planes* cling on to drifting seaweed and have become very widely distributed, particularly in the warmer parts of the world. The isopod *Idotea metallica* arrives occasionally in British waters, having been transported across the Atlantic by the North Atlantic Drift. But it is particularly the larval stages that are susceptible to dispersal by water currents, and which confer the advantages of wide distribution on species which have limited powers of locomotion when adult.

One striking example is the Robber Crab, *Birgus latro*, which, when adult, lives on land and is quite incapable of swimming. This crab has become widely dispersed all over the Indo-West Pacific region by virtue of its larvae, which are released into the sea by the females. The crab has thus managed to colonise remote islands that it could never have reached if it attempted to migrate as an adult.

The barnacles also provide a striking example, because their adult powers of locomotion are non-existent, although some do attach to driftwood and others to swimming animals (see p. 102).

Although water currents are the most frequent agents of dispersal of Crustacea they are by no means the only ones. Air currents and strong winds play a considerable part in the dispersal of small, fresh-water Crustacea which produce resting eggs capable of being dried. The wide dispersal of the Branchiopoda is to be accounted for in this way.

Biological agencies also play a part. The small eggs of Cladocera and ostracods can be transported very easily between the feathers of water birds. The presence of the South African ostracod, *Potamocypris humilis*, in a few rock pools on the south coast of Finland can be explained by its transport on the bodies of Arctic and Common Terns, which overwinter in South Africa and migrate to the Northern Hemisphere to breed. The evidence in this case is circumstantial, but there are other direct observations of the eggs of small Crustacea on birds.

Crustacea are also transported by insects. Ostracods have been found under the wings of the water boatman, *Notonecta*; small *Gammarus* sometimes attach to the large water beetle, *Dytiscus*, and the brackish water barnacle, *Balanus improvisus*, has been discovered attached to another large water beetle, *Hydrophilus piceus*. There is also a record of an Australian woodlouse being transported by a flying beetle.

The parthenogenetic species are the most likely to become successfully established after being transported. A single female hatching from a cladoceran ephippium can be the beginning of a large population if the environment proves to be suitable. It is the suitability of the environment which determines the distribution of the easily transportable species; they are not limited by their means of dispersal, but by their inability to survive in certain conditions.

Man has, both intentionally and unintentionally, aided in the distribution of Crustacea. His intentional activities have usually had commercial objectives. The introduction of the North American crayfish *Cambarus affinis* into Germany in 1890 has been followed by its introduction into Poland and France. In all these countries it has thrived and spread to form the basis of a profitable fishery.

Unintentional introductions into Europe include the Chinese River Crab, *Eriocheir sinensis*, and the barnacle *Elminius modestus*, which hails from the Antipodes. The former was probably brought over in ballast tanks, the latter attached itself to ships. A recent development in barnacle distribution is their attachment to the floats of sea planes; the period spent out of water would be no great hazard since the valves close and prevent desiccation.

All the terrestrial isopods of Newfoundland seem to have been transported there by man. Twelve species are known from the island, and not one is an endemic American species, but all are widely distributed in the Old World, especially in Western Europe. It is significant that five of the twelve species are known only from the Avalon Peninsula, where they seem to have arrived via the harbour of St. Johns. A further interesting point is that one of the most widespread woodlice of Newfoundland is the parthenogenetic form of *Trichoniscus pusillus*.

LITERATURE

BROOKS, J. L. (1950). Speciation in ancient lakes. *Quart. Rev. Biol.* 25: 30-60 and 131-176.

BRUNN, A. F. (1957). Deep sea and abyssal depths. In: *Treatise on marine ecology and paleoecology. Geol. Soc. Amer. Mem.* 67, vol. i, pp. 641-672.

CASPERS, H. (1957). Black Sea and Sea of Azov. In: *Treatise on marine ecology and paleoecology. Geol. Soc. Amer. Mem.* 67, vol. i, pp. 801-890.

CROGHAN, P. C. (1958). The osmotic and ionic regulation of *Artemia salina* (L.). *J. exp. Biol.* 35: 219-233.

EDNEY, E. B. (1954). Woodlice and the land habitat. *Biol. Rev.* 29: 185-219.

EKMAN, S. (1953). *Zoogeography of the sea.* London.

GORVETT, H. (1956). Tegumental glands and terrestrial life in wood-lice. *Proc. zool. Soc. Lond.* 126: 291-314.

HYNES, H. B. N. (1955). Distribution of some fresh-water Amphipoda in Britain. *Verh. int. Ver. Limnol.* 12: 620-628.

LONGHURST, A. R. (1955). A review of the Notostraca. *Bull. Brit. Mus. (Nat. Hist.) Zool.* 3: 3-57.

MARSHALL, N. B. (1954). *Aspects of deep sea biology.* London.

NAGEL, H. (1934). Die Aufgaben der Exretionsorgane und der Kiemen bei der Osmoregulation von Carcinus maenas. *Z. vergl. Physiol.* 21: 468-491.

PALMEN, E. (1951). A survey of the Oniscoidea (Isopoda Terr.) of Newfoundland. *Ann. Soc. zool. bot. fenn. Vanamo* 14 (1): 1-27.

PARRY, G. (1957). Osmoregulation in some fresh-water prawns. *J. exp. Biol.* 34: 417-423.

SEGERSTRALE, S. G. (1957). Baltic sea. In: *Treatise on marine ecology and paleoecology. Geol. Soc. Amer. Mem.* 67, vol. i, 751-800.

SPOONER, G. M. (1947). The distribution of *Gammarus* species in estuaries. Part 1. *J. mar. biol. Ass. U.K.* 27: 1-52.

SCHMIDT, W. L. (1942). The species of *Aegla*, endemic South American crustaceans. *Proc. U.S. Nat. Mus.* 91: 431-520.

ZENKEVICH, L. A. (1957). Caspian and Aral Seas. In: *Treatise on Marine ecology and paleoecology. Geol. Soc. Amer. Mem.* 67, vol. i, pp. 891-916.

CHAPTER X

CRUSTACEA AND MAN

M A N is probably the most omnivorous of all animals, and the wide range of his diet is reflected in the number of different Crustacea which he eats. The large decapods provide the greatest yields of edible meat per individual, but many other Crustacea can be caught in such vast numbers that, although they are negligible as individuals, in bulk they are of considerable value. Many of the smaller species are made into pastes; in Asia such pastes are made from true decapod shrimps, or mysids, or sometimes from Euphausiids. In North Africa even the brine shrimp, *Artemia salina*, is made into a paste and eaten with dates; this seems to be the only branchiopod eaten by man.

Barnacles, with their tough outer shells, do not seem to offer much to the gourmand, but in some parts of the world the soft body inside is eaten and appreciated. A species of the stalked form, *Pollicipes*, is eaten on the coasts of Spain and Brittany, while in Patagonia an acorn barnacle, *Balanus psittacus*, is eaten. This latter species is found as a particularly massive form on the coasts of Chile; the shell is cylindrical in shape, nearly eight inches in length and three inches in diameter, so that this species offers a meal comparable with a small lobster, and is reputed to be delicious in flavour.

Some species are only collected and eaten in restricted areas, and may be regarded as local delicacies, but others are esteemed over wide areas. One such is the giant mangrove swimming crab, *Scylla serrata*, which is sold in large numbers in the fish-markets on the east coast of Africa, and is enjoyed throughout the Indian and western Pacific oceans as far as Japan.

Methods of catching Crustacea are almost as varied as the Crustacea themselves. The most direct method is the search for the individual; this is of course only applicable to the large species, and usually takes a rather obvious form, but it is said that an experienced fisherman can collect large numbers of *Cancer pagurus* by finding the haunts of a newly moulted female

155

and removing the males which come to pay their attentions to her.

A unique method of catching crabs is reputed to be used on certain Pacific islands. The natives are said to fear the nipping powers of the Robber Crab, *Birgus latro*, but they also prize it as food, particularly the abdomen, which contains a lot of fat. This crab climbs trees, and when one is found up a tree the natives place a girdle of grass around the trunk at a considerable height above the ground. When the crab reaches the girdle on its way down it thinks that it has reached the ground and lets go of the tree. The fall stuns the crab, and the natives capture it. It is difficult to say how true this story is. The Robber Crab seems to be a particularly good subject for travellers' tales. One of these is the way in which it is supposed to open coconuts. The crab is stated to begin by tearing at the husk, always at the end under which the three eye-holes are situated. When this region is exposed the crab hammers one of the eye holes with its chelae until an opening is made. Then the crab turns round and puts its thin back legs, which bear small chelae, into the hole and removes the white material from inside. This tale has appeared in many otherwise reputable books, but a recent analysis of the evidence (Reyne, 1939), shows that the crab does not behave in this way. It does feed to some extent on coco-nuts, but only on those which have been damaged, in fact the natives on Guam use a coconut with a hole in it as bait for this crab. The Robber Crab feeds on other things such as carrion. Doubt may also be cast on the grass girdle method of capture, since Reyne found that the crab could fall from a height of five metres without harm.

Traps of various kinds are used for crabs and lobsters. The prin-ciple behind these is that access to the inside of the baited trap should be easy, and exit extremely difficult. The Cornish crab-pot is a familiar type; the Scots creel is a more convenient shape for stowing in a small boat. Local variations in the detailed structure of these traps are found. On the west coast of Scotland the creels are often 'one-eyed'—having only one entrance; in the Orkneys the creels have an additional anti-escape device in the form of a flap which open inwards when the lobster enters and closes behind it. The California spiny lobster fishermen use a type of creel made of wooden slats, without any netting. In Southern California it is reckoned that a crew of two with a fifteen-foot skiff can operate about 75 traps a day. The spiny lobster fishery is based entirely on the sale of living or freshly cooked specimens; pickling in any form is prohibited by law. This has led to the development of an air freight service from some of the fishing ports, so that living lobsters can be quickly transported inland. The relative value of the spiny lobster in Californian fisheries can be judged from the fact that although rated twenty-first by poundage the lobster was rated eleventh in monetary value in 1946.

Modern methods are also used by the Russians, who have floating canneries operating in the Arctic and North Pacific Oceans; their produce includes canned crab which can be bought at some of the better food stores in London.

When a fishing industry becomes highly organised there is always the danger that the stock may be reduced to such a level as to make fishing uneconomical. This is guarded against by various laws. In Britain no lobster under nine inches in length should be offered for sale, and any lobster carrying eggs must be returned to the sea. In South California there is a closed season for the spiny lobster from March 15th to October 1st, and the minimum size permitted to be sold is a length of 10 inches; a maximum length of 16 inches is also applied here. This is probably a good method of ensuring a high reproductive rate, because a female of 16 inches or over can carry well over 500,000 eggs, while smaller females carry fewer. The restriction of maximum size does not affect the market, because it has been found that the middle-sized lobsters are in the greatest demand.

Fishermen in Southern Spain practise a different type of regulation of their crab fisheries. The male of a local crab, *Uca tangeri*, produces a very large chela, which the fishermen snap off and then put the crab back in the sea to grow another; only the claws are sent to market.

The smaller Crustacea are generally caught in nets, which vary tremendously in design and size in different parts of the world. In Brunei Bay, North Borneo, two men can operate a small boat and a net called a rambat udang, which is cast by hand. This net is made of cotton thread, and is started by making a circle of 35 meshes, a number which is supposed to make the net lucky. The large shrimp industries rely less on luck and use trawl nets up to 135 feet across, operated from trawlers 50-70 feet long and equipped with fathometers, navigational aids, radios, and enough ice to keep the shrimps fresh for a couple of weeks. Using nets and boats of this sort the Texas shrimp fishery landed over 79 million pounds of shrimps, mainly *Penaeus* species, during the season 1954-55.

Shrimps are also caught in fixed 'engines' on the shore. These are wide-mouthed conical nets or baskets arranged with the mouths facing the ebb tide. Large numbers of such traps may be arranged to form an almost solid wall, so that a large volume of water passes through them, leaving the shrimps trapped in the narrow end. Variants of such traps are found throughout the world, from the Severn Estuary to Singapore.

An interesting addition to the normal commercial fishery in Texas has recently appeared. The increased interest in sea-fishing for sport has led to a demand for live bait, and shrimps are very suitable for this purpose, particularly as they form over 70 per cent of the food of some sport fish, such as the speckled sea trout (*Cynoscion nebulosus*). The bait shrimpers operate smaller nets, and use them for short periods, since they are not trying to catch great numbers, but want moderate numbers in good condition. The bait boats are often equipped with tanks and running sea water for transporting the shrimps, others merely place the shrimps in a live box which is towed behind the boat.

The use of crabs as bait has been long established on the Northern Adriatic shores of Jugoslavia. Here the common shore crab (*Carcinus maenas*) is ground up and used as a lure for shoals of sardines.

Crustacean meat is relatively valuable. A comparison with one of the most valuable marine fish, the sole, *Solea solea*, gives an idea of the value of the Crustacea eaten in Britain. In 1955 the sole was valued at £13 6s. 5d. per cwt., lobsters at £19 8s. 6d. per cwt., and prawns at £33 1s. 1d. per cwt. Crabs were much less valuable at £3 11s. 4d. per cwt., so were shrimps at £4 0s. 11d. per cwt. These weights include the shells, and the lower value of crabs and shrimps is probably due to the greater labour involved in preparing a given weight of edible meat, as well as to the superior flavour of prawns and lobsters.

The prices of Crustacea in Britain have risen sharply over the last twenty years. To take only a couple of examples: in 1938 shrimps were valued at £1 9s. 3d. a cwt., while prawns were £18 9s. 8d. a cwt., these prices form a sharp contrast with those quoted for 1955. The Norway lobster, *Nephrops norvegicus*, has also increased rapidly in price during the last few years. The price in Scotland rose from £1 17s. 0d. a cwt. in 1950 to £3 12s. 0d. a cwt. in 1952; the average price in Britain during 1955 was £4 4s. 7d., compared with £1 4s. 6d. per cwt. in 1938.

So far we have been dealing with Crustacea as the direct food of man, but they are probably of more importance as indirect food, because they form a substantial part of the food of fish, particularly the young stages of marine fish. Here are a few examples, almost at random, from the large number available.

On the trawling grounds off Plymouth the young stages of the poor cod, *Gadus minutus*, feed almost entirely on copepods, particularly *Pseudocalanus elongatus*. The adults feed to a large extent on decapods, though fish may form up to fifty per cent of the food.

Baby pike, *Esox lucius*, in Windermere, feed mostly on small Crustacea, but once a pike reaches a length of an inch and a half it begins to feed on small fish.

A survey of the feeding habits of young fish of the herring family from waters near Bombay showed that Crustacea formed at least fifty per cent, often much more, of the food of nearly all the sixteen species examined.

Sometimes, for part of a year, a single crustacean species may form the food of a fish. A striking example has been observed in the Baltic. On the south-west coast of Finland the smelt (*Osmerus eperlanus*) feeds on mysids for most of the year, but during the period from mid-November to mid-December most of its food consists of mature males of the amphipod *Pontoporeia affinis*. This peculiar situation is explained by the fact that *Pontoporeia* is mainly a bottom-dwelling creature, but during the short winter breeding season the males become active swimmers and so attract the attention of the smelt.

Other important benefits that man gains from the Crustacea are the products of the whaling industry. The most important whales are those which have whalebone strainers inside the edges of their mouths and feed on medium-sized Crustacea which they strain out of the water. In the Antarctic the most important of the whale food species is *Euphausia superba*, which forms enormous shoals in the summer.

Some seals also feed on Crustacea, and then in turn provide food or clothing for man. There are also records of terrestrial mammals feeding on Crustacea, perhaps the most surprising of these is the habit of the wild swine near Trincomali, Ceylon, which come down to the shore each night and dig up crabs.

Another use that man has found for Crustacea is to provide food for his pet fish. Living *Daphnia* is sold by aquarium dealers, and is generally regarded as an excellent food for goldfish. The keen aquarist can easily culture his own stocks of *Daphnia* to provide an occasional treat for his pets. The easiest method is to keep water snails and feed them on any waste greenery that they will take. The faeces produced by the snails make excellent food for *Daphnia*, which will thrive in a tank well stocked with snails. An alternative is to keep axolotls which are fed on earthworms. If a glass tank containing axolotls is stood near a window there will be an abundant growth of microscopic algae which will form a good food for *Daphnia*. A separate tank is necessary for the water fleas because if kept with the axolotls they will be snapped up and eaten. Every day or two a sample of green water from the axolotl tank should be poured into the *Daphnia* tank and then replaced by fresh water from the tap. In this way a continuous culture can be maintained right through the winter.

Daphnia is also dried and sold in packets as fish food. One important centre of this minor industry is in northern Italy. This is believed to date from the time when Bologna goldfish were highly esteemed and the water fleas were used to sustain the fish while they were transported home by tourists.

The brine shrimp, *Artemia salina*, is another crustacean used by aquarists. The resting eggs (see p. 72) are sold in small tubes, with instructions how to make them hatch. The nauplii which emerge are used as food for tropical fish. Drying and packing these eggs is a profitable business in North America, where, in certain localities, particularly around the Great Salt Lake, eggs can be collected by the shovelful. The small tubes, containing about a teaspoonful, cost about half a crown to buy in a shop, but even a small tubeful of eggs will provide several thousand nauplii. These nauplii can be reared through to adults if they are kept in sea water and fed on small amounts of yeast which has been stirred up well in water before being poured in with *Artemia*.

If sea water is not available a substitute can be made from Tidman's sea salt, which can be purchased from any chemist's. About four ounces of salt to six pints of water will produce a suitable concentration for rearing *Artemia*.

When kept in a warm room *Artemia* becomes mature in about three weeks and will then start to produce nauplii. These can be fished out with a small net and used as fish food while the stock is maintained by further production of nauplii by the adults. A regular supply of fish food can be maintained by judicious management of such a stock, taking care to leave a few nauplii to reach maturity and keep up the breeding strength.

Some Crustacea are the direct cause of economic loss to man. The fouling of ships by barnacles might at first sight seem a trivial matter, but a heavy layer of fouling can increase, by about fifty per cent, the amount of fuel needed to maintain a given speed. Such increased costs of transport will be reflected in the increased price of goods when they eventually appear for sale in shops.

The important species causing fouling are *Balanus crenatus* in temperate water, *B. amphitrite* and *B. tintinnabulum* in warmer waters. As a general rule the tropics are the worst areas for the fouling of ships; the polar regions are comparatively clean in this respect. Settlement only occurs when ships are in port; when a ship is moving the cypris larvae cannot establish themselves and the hull remains clean. Natural control of fouling can be achieved by avoiding long stays in tropical ports and by arranging that the ship visits fresh-water ports, where the barnacles are killed. The death of the barnacles does not get rid of their tough outer shells; this can be done by visiting a scouring port. In such ports, for instance Calcutta, the water carries a lot of sand which effectively scours the side of the ship and wears down the barnacles. This method has to be used with caution, obviously the scouring action will not restrict itself to the barnacles, and too long a stay in a scouring port may necessitate repainting the hull to resist corrosion.

The painting of ships' hulls is done primarily to prevent corrosion of the metal by sea water, and secondarily to reduce fouling by poisoning the organisms concerned. Anti-fouling paints are designed to liberate poisons in sufficient amounts to kill any cyprids settling on the surface. Such paints cannot of course last for ever; the best ones are those which liberate the poisons at a rate which is only just sufficient for their purpose and so make for a longer interval between repaintings.

The poisons used in anti-fouling paints are often compounds of copper or mercury. Mixtures of compounds of these two heavy metals have been found to give better results than compounds of each metal used separately. Organic compounds of mercury are often much more toxic than its inorganic compounds; n-amyl mercuric chloride is twenty times as toxic as mercuric chloride to the nauplii of *Elminius modestus*. To some extent the toxicity of organomercuric compounds is related to their solubility in fats; this may be important, because the poisons appear to act by penetrating

M

through the cuticle and this will usually involve passing a layer containing fats. The exact mode of action of these poisons is not known, but mercury is known to inhibit the action of certain enzymes, so that a general interference with metabolism may be the end result. When compounds of mercury have been tested on prawns large amounts of the poisons have been found in the excretory organs, suggesting that the crustacean body makes an attempt to rid itself of the toxic material.

Damage by marine boring animals is also of great economic importance, and of all the creatures responsible for such damage two are outstanding: one is a mollusc, *Teredo*, the ship-worm; the other is an isopod crustacean, *Limnoria*, the gribble. There are some fourteen wood-boring species of *Limnoria* known, and a further seven are known which burrow in the holdfasts of large seaweeds.

Piles supporting wharfs and piers seem to be particularly susceptible to damage by marine borers. It has been estimated that the annual damage around the coasts of the U.S.A. amounts to over fifty million dollars. The gribble seems able to attack creosote-impregnated wood earlier than the ship-worm. It makes shallow tunnels along the grain of the wood and this allows water to penetrate further into the wood and leach out more of the protective creosote.

Wood which is exposed to the sea is quickly attacked by a variety of fungi, and it is probable that such an attack is necessary before the gribble can successfully establish itself. Adult gribbles die in about four days if they are kept with sterile wood in sterile water, but they live for much longer periods if fed on cultures of a marine fungus. Another indication of the importance of fungi as food for *Limnoria* is revealed when the amino-acid constitution of the fungus and the isopod are compared. The fungus, *Lulworthia floridana*, contains the same thirteen amino acids as *Limnoria tripunctata*, from which the gut has been removed to avoid contamination. Sterile pinewood only contains seven of these acids, However the gribble also obtains some nutriment from the wood, and its gut contains enzymes which are capable of digesting cellulose and other substances in wood.

Infestation of new wood is carried out by sexually mature gribbles, but the females are not carrying eggs when they migrate to the new habitat. Pairing occurs after they have become established in their new burrows. Each burrow usually contains a female at the point of active extension, and a male a little further back. The young, which emerge from the female brood pouch as miniature adults, start their own burrows from the side of the parental burrow. Each female may produce three broods of twenty or thirty young in a season, so that extensive damage can be inflicted in a couple of seasons. Attacks are generally most severe at low water mark, and the damaged piles often taper towards their bases, like well-sharpened pencils.

An amphipod, *Chelura terebrans*, is also found in burrows in piling, but it does not seem to be a very good borer on its own, and usually relies on the activities of the gribble to provide it with a home.

Another crustacean activity detrimental to man is the transmission of diseases. In general the Crustacea are not very important from this point of view, but in the tropics they play a part in the life cycles of some objectionable parasites. One of these is the guinea worm, *Dracunculus medinensis*, which is a large nematode, or roundworm, reaching a length of three or four feet. The adults live in the tissues just under the skin of man, and the females liberate living young through ulcers, usually on the legs of the host. The young are liberated when the host limbs are in water, and they can swim quite actively. Further development occurs when the small worms are swallowed by a copepod, *Cyclops*. After three weeks in *Cyclops* the worms are then in an infective state and when *Cyclops* is swallowed by man with his drinking water the cycle is completed.

The largest of the tapeworms which infect man also has an intermediate stage in a copepod. *Diphyllobothrium latum*, the broad tapeworm, reaches a length of sixty feet. Man becomes infected by eating raw or insufficiently cooked fish, and the fish becomes infected either by swallowing an infected *Cyclops*, or by eating another fish that has eaten an infected *Cyclops*. In this case the copepod is not the direct transmitter to man, but is once or twice removed down the line of intermediate hosts. A more direct transmission of a parasitic worm is found in certain river crabs. In various parts of the old world these crabs are infected with the larval stages of a fluke, or flatworm, of the genus *Paragonimus*. These live as adults in the lungs of man, and the eggs are ejected with sputum. A larval stage emerges from the egg and infects a snail, eventually giving rise to a different type of larva. These larvae infect river crabs and crayfish, and the infection passes to man when these crustacea are eaten raw. The young worms make their way through the wall of the gut and migrate up into the lungs.

M*

Crustacea also play a part in the biology of water supply. Reservoirs are often ideal places for the growth of small planktonic algae, some of which can cause the water to become coloured, or to taste unpleasant. Fortunately the algae are usually kept in check by small planktonic Crustacea, particularly the Cladocera. These in turn can cause a certain amount of trouble when they block the filters at waterworks. There have been occasions on which a waterworks engineer has been heard to curse *Daphnia longispina* and *Bosmina* while frantically searching for an alternate supply of water to the suburban areas for which he is responsible. The Cladocera had choked his filters and suburban man would be watering his garden that evening, making heavy demands on the supply.

Onchocerciasis will serve as a final example of the indirect ways in which Crustacea impinge on the affairs of man. The causal organism of this disease is a nematode, *Onchocerca*, which lives under the skin of man, and has the distressing tendency of migrating into the eyes, eventually causing blindness. Over a large part of Africa this nematode is transmitted by the bite of a fly appropriately called *Simulium damnosum*. The aim in controlling the disease is to eliminate the fly by killing off its larvae. This can only be done when the habits of the larvae are known; they live attached to stones in swift flowing rivers, but in the hilly part of Kenya, near Lake Victoria, the disease is transmitted by another species of *Simulium, S. neavi*, and for many years the larva of this species could not be found, although all the likely places were searched by competent entomologists. Eventually, it was discovered that the larvae habitually attach themselves to the backs of river crabs. These crustaceans had innocently thwarted the efforts of medical entomologists throughout the years of searching, and delayed the beginning of control measures designed to save many people from blindness.

LITERATURE

ANDERSON, A. M., HEADLY, D. & TUBB, J. A. (1953). Notes on the fisheries industry of Brunei Bay and Labuan Island. *Proc. Indo-Pacific Fisheries Council. 4th Meeting*, Sect. II, pp. 146-165.

GUEST, W. C. (1956). The Texas shrimp fishery. *Texas Game and Fish Commission Bulletin*, No. 36: 1-23.

MENZIES, R. J. (1957). The marine borer family Limnoriidae (Crustacea, Isopoda). *Bull. mar. Sci. Gulf Caribb.* 7: 101-200.

MISTAKIDIS, M. N. (1957). The biology of *Pandalus montagui.* Leach. *Fisheries Investigations* (2) 21 (4): 1-52. H.M.S.O.

PYEFINCH, K. A. (1947). The biology of ship fouling. *New Biology* 3: 128-148.

REYNE, A. (1939). On the food habits of the Coconut Crab (*Birgus latro* L.) with notes on its distribution. *Arch. Neerl. Zool.* 3:

SEGERSTRALE, S. G. (1950). The amphipods on the coasts of Finland —some facts and problems. *Comment. Biol. Helsingf.* 10 (4): 1-28.

Sea Fisheries Statistical Tables. London, H.M.S.O.

WILSON, R. C. (1948). A review of the Southern California spiny lobster fishery. *Calif. Fish and Game* 34: 71-80.

APPENDIX

A classification of Crustacea to show the systematic position of most of the genera mentioned in the text

Order Monstrilloida—fam. Monstrillidae.
Order Cyclopoida—*Afrocyclops, Ascomyzon, Cyclops, Eucy-
clops, Macrocyclops, Microcyclops, Micropontius, Mytili-
cola, Oithona, Orthocyclops, Thersitina.*
Order Harpacticoida—*Afrocamptus, Dactylopusioides, Penta-
camptus, Sunaristes, Thalestris, Tisbe.*
Order Notodelphyoida—*Ascidicola.*
Order Caligoida—*Eudactylina, Lepeophtheirus, Lernanthropus,
Trebius.*
Order Lernaeoida—*Brachiella, Chondracanthus, Lernaea,
Lernaeocera.*
Order Herpyllobioida—*Aspidoecia, Rhizorhina, Sphaeronella,
Sphaeronellopsis, Xenocoeloma.*

SUB CLASS BRANCHIURA
Order Branchiura—*Argulus, Chonopeltis, Dolops.*

SUB CLASS MALACOSTRACA
Division Phyllocarida
Order Nahecarida—*Nahecaris* (fossil only).
Order Leptostraca—*Nebalia, Nebaliopsis.*
Division Hoplocarida
Order Stomatopoda—*Coronida, Squilla.*
Division Syncarida
Order Bathynellacea—*Bathynella.*
Order Anaspidacea—*Anaspides.*
Division Thermosbaenida
Order Thermosbaenacea—*Monodella, Thermosbaena.*
Division Peracarida
Order Spelaeogriphacea—*Spelaeogriphus.*
Order Mysidacea—*Gnathomysis, Gnathophausia, Hemimysis,
Heteromysis, Lophogaster, Mysis, Pseudomysis, Siriella,
Troglomysis.*
Order Cumacea—*Diastylis, Pseudocuma.*
Order Amphipoda—*Ampelisca, Bathporeia, Bruzelia, Chelura,
Corophium, Cyamus, Cyclocaris, Cystisoma, Gammarus,
Haustorius, Hyalella, Hyperia, Marinogammarus,
Onisimus, Phronima, Pontogammarus, Pontoporeia,
Pseudalibrotus, Pseudoprotella, Talitroides, Trischizos-
toma.*
Order Tanaidacea—*Herpotanais, Neotanais, Tanais.*

Order Isopoda.

Sub order Flabellifera—*Bathygnathia, Bathynomus, Caecosphaeroma, Eurydice, Gnathia, Limnoria, Microlistra, Paragnathia, Sphaeroma.*

Sub order Valvifera—*Antarcturus, Idotea, Mesidotea.*

Sub order Asellota—*Asellus, Macrostylis.*

Sub order Oniscoidea—*Armadillidium, Kogmania, Ligia, Oniscus, Platyarthrus, Porcellio, Schoblia, Trichoniscus, Tylos.*

Sub order Phreatoicidea—*Phreatoicus.*

Sub order Epicaridea—*Bopyrus, Danalia, Liriopsis, Pinnotherion.*

Division Eucarida

Order Euphausiacea—*Euphausia.*

Order Decapoda

Sub order Natantia

Tribe Penaeida—*Penaeus, Sergestes.*

Tribe Stenopodidea—*Spongicola.*

Tribe Caridea—*Crangon, Hymenodora, Hippolyte, Lysmata, Macrobrachium, Palaemon* (=*Leander*), *Palaemonetes, Paratypton, Processa, Sclerocrangon, Spirontocaris, Systellaspis, Xiphocaridina.*

Sub order Reptantia

Tribe Astacura—*Astacoides, Astacopsis, Cambaroides, Cambarus, Engaeus, Homarus, Nephrops, Orconectes, Parastacus, Potamobius, Thaumastocheles, Troglocambarus.*

Tribe Palinura—*Jassus, Palinurus, Panulirus, Parribacus, Polycheles, Stereomastis.*

Tribe Anomura—*Aegla, Birgus, Callianassa, Coenobita, Eupagurus, Galathea, Hippa, Lithodes, Pagurus, Parapagurus, Porcellana, Thalassina, Upogebia.*

Tribe Brachyura—*Atlantotlos, Calappa, Cancer, Carcinus, Carpilius, Carpoporus, Eriocheir, Eumedon, Gecarcinus, Grapsus, Huenia, Hyas, Lissocarcinus, Lupa, Lupella, Lybia, Macrocheira, Macropodia, Maia, Mithrax, Myra, Oregonia, Pinnotheres, Planes, Platymaia, Polybius, Portunus, Rhithropanopeus, Scylla, Sesarma, Telphusa, Thalamita, Uca, Ucides.*

INDEX

Page numbers in italics refer to text figures.

Wilson, D. P., 96, 97
Wilson, R. C., 165
woodlice, 94, 95, 96, 105, 147, 152, 153
worms, 63, 110, 112, 116

Xanthidae, 129
xanthopterin, 55
Xenocoeloma, 110
Xiphocaridina compressa, 54

X-organ, 58, 64
X-rays, 70

Y-organ, 64, 65, 67
Yonge, C. M., 81, 83

Zenkevich, L. A., 154
zoea, 76, 77